The British Waterfowl Association

# British Waterfowl
# Standards

The British Waterfowl Association

# British Waterfowl Standards

Complete specifications and judging points of all standardized
breeds and varieties of domestic waterfowl compiled by the
British Waterfowl Association and recognized by the Poultry Club
of Great Britain

**Illustrated by**
Carl Donner

**Edited by**
Chris Ashton, BA, Ph.D.
Mike Ashton, BA, MA

**Managing Editor**
Christopher Marler, F.Z.S., F.L.S.

**Standards Committee Members**
John Hall
Stephanie Mansell
W.R.Sumner

The British
Waterfowl
Association

CONSERVATION
PRESERVATION
EDUCATION

*B.W.A founded as the Waterfowl Club in 1887*
*Registered Charity No. 263156*

Published by The British Waterfowl Association
© Copyright 1999 The British Waterfowl Association
ISBN 0 9503378 2 X

Produced for The British Waterfowl Association by
The Senecio Press, Charlbury, England.

# Contents

# Foreword

Following the publication of the 1982 Poultry Club Standards, which introduced new descriptions for several breeds of waterfowl, Tom Bartlett suggested that the *British Waterfowl Association* should produce its own illustrated Standards. Paintings could give better definition than photographs, and a special edition would mark the increasing popularity of waterfowl and the greater number of standardized breeds available in Britain.

The artist Carl Donner was commissioned to paint the watercolour pictures and the number of breeds that he has been asked to complete has, of course, increased over the several years that it has taken to produce this work. Carl is himself a waterfowl breeder of considerable experience and success. He is particularly well known for his Calls and Cayugas.

Since this was to be a special 'one off' edition, a review of the Standards took place. The Standards Committee was formed consisting of Chris Ashton (Chairperson), Mike Ashton, John Hall, Stephanie Mansell and Billy Sumner. They have been successful breeders, exhibitors and judges of waterfowl in the 1980s and 90s. John Hall in particular has a wealth of experience in a lifetime's work with both domestics and wildfowl. This committee drafted the new layout and consulted many BWA members in writing, as well as orally, on their views during the period 1996-97. We also acknowledge the co-operation given by the Poultry Club Council and in particular the members of the Poultry Club/BWA Liaison Committee—John Breslain, Victoria Roberts and Malcolm Thompson—in advising on the final layout of this specialist section of Poultry.

The whole project has only finally come to fruition because of the input of many members of the BWA pooling their skills, knowledge and expertise in the world of waterfowl. Financial backing has also been kindly offered by several members with longstanding interest in the BWA in order to bring this project forward to mark the millennium, and gain the best terms for the Association.

# Introduction

## The First Standards

The need for any form of unified standards for the judging of exhibition poultry was not really apparent until the middle of the nineteenth century. The first *Standard of Excellence in Exhibition Poultry* was authorized by the Poultry Society in 1865. In addition to the poultry, it contained only six breeds of ducks and geese, and there was a fifteen point scale to aid the judging. It was at this time also that Lewis Wright was formulating his monumental work *The Illustrated Book of Poultry*, which marked an upsurge of interest in domestic fowl. This book sought to provide encyclopaedic knowledge of the birds, their origins, characteristics and utility aspects. Shortly afterwards, the Poultry Club decided to assert itself as the official guardian of poultry quality and published the first *Poultry Club Standards* in 1886 expanding the formal description of the breeds and using a one hundred point scale for judging. It followed similar moves by the American Poultry Association, which had published their standards in February 1874.

Why this should occur all at this time is largely a product of the on-going processes of the Agrarian and Industrial Revolutions that had begun roughly one hundred years earlier. An interest in mass-production of food was made necessary to feed the large influx of population into the industrial cities. Communities were no longer self-sufficient and large quantities of ducks and geese, amongst other things, were needed for transporting into places like London. This led in turn to locations of specialist producers like Aylesbury for ducks and East Anglia for geese.

Exhibitions too were not just a pleasant hobby. They were the shop-window for the commercial producers. In 1845 the first National Poultry Show was held at the Zöological Gardens in London. There were classes incidentally for 'Common Geese, Asiatic and Knobbed Geese, and Any Other Variety'. The difference between this show and previous ones was that the birds were now shown live rather than dressed for the table.

The fashionable interest in live exhibition coincided with the importation of exotic creatures from all over the globe. It was the age, after all, of the zöological garden which found its way into the hearts and vocabulary of the people in the form of the 'zoo'. There was a collecting mania for insects, birds, mammals, reptiles and plants. This was the age of Kew Gardens and also the age of Darwin. The great empires of Britain, France and Germany were sending home many new creatures, including new breeds of ducks, geese, chickens, pheasants and other fowl. All this was of course fuelled by coal and transported rapidly by sea and rail.

The exhibitions, which set up monuments like the Eiffel Tower and the Crystal Palace, also attempted to attain encyclopaedic knowledge as well as eclectic displays. This was the great era of classification, description and objective measuring. People wanted a certain permanence and finality to their affluent and stable lives. Encapsulating the various breeds in Standards of Perfection was one way of doing this. It attempted to arrest change and prevent decay—'keeping up the standard'. It also attempted to provide laws and a level arena for the cut and thrust of exhibition rivalry.

The next stage in the development of waterfowl production was a natural continuation from earlier stages. New and exotic breeds like the Indian Runner and Pekin Ducks led to even newer cross-breeds in the late nineteenth and early parts of the twentieth century. Extra vigour, size, fertility and egg-laying potential became the incentives for more and more variants. There were the Campbells, Orpingtons and Abacot Rangers. All of these birds are little more than crossings and re-crossings with Runners in particular. They added to the kudos of their creators and enabled phenomenal mass-production. The Campbells, for example, achieved an average of 223 eggs per bird over a 48 week period in the 1922-24 Bentley laying tests. Such mass production is typical of the age that generated the Poultry Standards.

## The 1999 BWA Standards

This version of Waterfowl Standards has been produced by the BWA to accompany a limited edition of *The Histories of the Standard Breeds of Domestic Waterfowl*. In both publications, paintings by Carl Donner have been used in preference to photographs of individual birds. It was felt that the paintings would illustrate the colour and form of the breeds, giving a better indication of type than an individual specimen which would be unlikely to have all the ideal characteristics and may even embody several faults.

Standards for waterfowl have now evolved over more than a century and, since 1865, information about new breeds and colours has been added to a rather informal framework. Descriptions have come from America (in the case of the Pilgrim) and from the Continent (for the Saxony and Steinbacher). There are now thirty-seven breeds of waterfowl and many colours for some of these breeds. It seemed time to establish a more rational layout to the Standards.

During the period from 1996-97 the Waterfowl Standards were extensively reviewed by a committee which consulted widely in writing with established waterfowl breeders and judges. Whilst the standard format was changed, the 1982 wording of the content was adhered to as closely as possible. In the process of discussion, the language was simplified to eliminate repetition, in some breeds; in others, more detail was added where it was felt that the original was rather cursory or imprecise.

The points system had evolved over many years from different sources and had been applied in different ways to different breeds. It was therefore re-organized to be more useful to judges and breeders rather than as a complex memory test. Thus, prior to the publication of the 1997 Poultry Club Standards, there was a partial review of the points scale for the geese. There was not time to deal with the more extensive and chaotic scheme for the ducks. As a result, a final review had to be deferred until this edition.

The description of the birds now begins conventionally at the top and works its way down from the head to the feet, as did Chaucer in c.1398 with his detailed description of a chicken. This was also used in the Poultry Club Standards of 1926 when the term 'body' actually described the torso of the bird. Later the term was transformed into 'type' which is ordinarily understood to be a holistic concept.

The 1982 Standards, for example, used 'type' in the following ways:

**Black East Indian**

| | |
|---|---|
| Type | 20 |
| Size | 20 |
| Head, bill and neck | 15 |
| Legs and feet | 5 |
| Colour | 30 |
| Condition | 10 |

When we look at the definition of type in the 'General Characteristics' we see 'Type: Body short and broad. Breast round and prominent'. Clearly 'type' is merely synonymous with 'body'. On the other hand the **Indian Runner** had:

| | |
|---|---|
| Body—shape and general appearance of, including lower part of neck, legs and feet | 35 |
| Carriage and action | 30 |
| Head, eyes, bill and neck, exclusive of lower neck expansion | 20 |
| Colour and condition | 15 |

Only the **Toulouse** had anything remotely like our normal definition of 'type':

| | |
|---|---|
| Type (head and throat 15, breast and keel 10, tail, stern and paunch 10, neck 5, general carriage 15) | 55 |
| Size | 20 |
| Legs and feet | 5 |
| Colour and markings | 10 |
| Condition | 10 |

The Greek word 'tupos' is said to mean 'impression or figure'. It is closely related to the concept of something being 'stamped' and therefore a fixed model. Modern dictionaries give many definitions of 'type', some of which are of direct relevance to the present case: biologically, an organism having or chosen as having the essential characteristics of its group; a person, thing, or event serving as an illustration, symbol, or characteristic specimen of another, or of a class; an object, conception, or work of art serving as a model for subsequent artists. When applied to poultry all of these definitions have two things in common: typicality and wholeness. By these we mean that the 'type' identifies what is characteristic (typical) of the breed of birds, and also what characterizes the *whole* bird if it is to be the model.

Unfortunately slight differences in emphasis can result in radical misinterpretations of meaning. In 1905 *The American Standard of Perfection* applied both meanings to poultry judging: 'Typical—Expressing a characteristic, in colour or form, representative of a breed or variety—for example, typical shape, meaning the form peculiar to a breed.' By 1993 the idea of colour being part of type seems to have been dropped. The new *American Standard of Perfection* gives type as 'The general shape and form common to all members of a breed resulting from the breeding to an ideal shape and size as set forth in the Standard of Perfection.' The 1997 Poultry Club Standards is rather succinct: 'Type: mould or shape (see 'Symmetry')'. Symmetry is described as 'Perfection of outline, proportion; harmony of all parts'.

7

The over-riding impression is that 'type' is something to do with the whole form, what psychologists call the *gestalt*. It must, by definition, include all elements of the shape of the animal and may even refer to the carriage. It is almost impossible to conceive of a typical Indian Runner or Pekin Duck without reference to its upright posture. This is a vital ingredient of its shape. Thus where, in both the 'General Characteristics' and 'Scale of Points', the 1982 Poultry Club Standards has used 'type' as a synonym for 'body', we have chosen to substitute the latter word and have reserved 'type' for the overall shape.

When it comes to aggregating points or differentiating the weaknesses of different birds, it is not logical to deal with the vague concept in a subjective way. [Gestalt is defined as being 'an organized whole that is perceived as *more than the sum of its parts*'.] It is necessary therefore to indicate precisely what makes one bird more deviant from 'type' than another. 'Type' in this context is said to be the total number of points constituting the head, neck, body, legs, feet, and carriage *where it affects the outline of the bird*. Obviously the relative importance of these components will vary from breed to breed, and this is why some breeds are allocated more points than others for specific elements, like head (in Crested Ducks) or carriage (in Indian Runner Ducks). All aspects of colour (plumage, legs, beak, eyes, etc.) are covered separately under the section 'Colour'.

To aid in the use of these Standards, the description and points generally follow the same order, except where conflation helps description. Conflation generally follows the same order, without side headings. The order for colour follows that of the Rouen, except where traditional descriptions have limited this.

As far as measurements are concerned, we have followed the 1997 Poultry Club Standards, using metric first followed by Imperial in brackets. As a concession to those more used to pounds we have retained whole numbers in the Imperial measurements and therefore have had to use less rounded metric figures.

Defects, deformities and disqualifications have been subject to a little change. Specific defects have not been included in the colour and type descriptions. They have been mainly confined to a specific 'Defects' section. There are a few exceptions to this where it has helped to clarify the text. A judge is expected to penalize any bird which is deficient in breed characteristics to such an extent that it is an unworthy specimen of the breed.

Deformities and defects, which impair the well-being of the bird, inevitably creep into any restricted gene pool. Specimens which carry an obvious deformity should be heavily penalized or disqualified. Both breeders and newcomers to the fancy need to be aware of the dangers of such defects, which are mentioned only where they are known to be a particular recurring problem at present.

Common physical problems are:
• beak malformation
• blindness
• lack of co-ordination
• spinal deformity (kinked neck, roach or twisted back, wry tail)
• wing defects (e.g. oar wing)
• feet defects (e.g. crooked toes)

As a foot-note, we need to explain that we have not felt it necessary, in each breed, to explain that domestic waterfowl have webbed feet, nor that drakes have mallard sex curls.

# Classification of breeds
## and date standardized in Great Britain

## Geese

| Heavy | | Medium | | Light | |
|---|---|---|---|---|---|
| African (brown) | 1982 | Brecon Buff | 1954 | Chinese (brown) | 1954 |
| African (buff) | 1999 | Buff Back | 1982 | Chinese (white) | 1954 |
| African (white) | 1982 | Grey Back | 1982 | Pilgrim | 1982 |
| American Buff | 1982 | Pomeranian | 1982 | Roman | 1954 |
| Embden | 1865 | West of England | 1999 | Sebastopol (white) | 1982 |
| Toulouse (grey) | 1865 | | | Sebastopol (frizzle) | 1997 |
| Toulouse (white) | 1982 | | | Sebastopol (buff) | 1997 |
| Toulouse (buff) | 1997 | | | Steinbacher | 1997 |

## Ducks

| Heavy | | Light | | Indian Runner | |
|---|---|---|---|---|---|
| Aylesbury | 1865 | Abacot Ranger | 1997 | Black | 1930 |
| Blue Swedish | 1982 | Bali | 1930 | Chocolate | 1930 |
| Cayuga | ?1886 | Campbell (khaki) | 1926 | Cumberland Blue | 1982 |
| Muscovy | 1954 | Campbell (white) | 1954 | Fawn | ?1922 |
| Pekin | ?1886 | Campbell (dark) | 1954 | Fawn & White | 1901 |
| Rouen | 1865 | Crested | ?1922 | American | |
| Rouen Clair | 1982 | Hook Bill | 1997 | Fawn & White | 1997 |
| Saxony | 1982 | Magpie (black&white) | 1926 | Mallard | 1982 |
| Silver Appleyard | 1982 | Magpie (blue&white) | 1982 | Trout | 1982 |
| | | Magpie (dun&white) | 1997 | White | ?1922 |
| | | Orpington (buff) | ?1922 | | |
| | | Welsh Harlequin* | 1997 | | |

| Bantam | | Call | |
|---|---|---|---|
| Black East Indian | 1865 | Apricot | 1997 |
| Crested Miniature | 1997 | Bibbed | 1997 |
| Silver Appleyard Miniature | 1997 | Blue Fawn | 1982 |
| Silver Bantam | 1982# | Dark Silver | 1999 |
| | | Magpie | 1997 |
| | | Mallard | 1865 |
| | | Pied | 1982 |
| | | Silver | 1982 |
| | | White | 1865 |

*The 1982 standard erroneously described the Whaylesbury
# a.k.a. Silver Appleyard Bantam 1982

The dates refer to *Poultry Club* Standards after 1865

# Geese

The first poultry show of 1845 classified Common Geese, Asiatic or Knob Geese and 'Any other variety'. The first Book of Standards in 1865 described the Toulouse and the Embden. These two breeds monopolized our standards up to recent times, being the chief ones exhibited regularly at shows. At times, other breeds have been exhibited and now the standards have been extended.

The greylag is said to be the ancestor of all our domestic geese originating in Europe. The Common goose, according to Harrison Weir, was either white or grey. The colour may have been sex-linked. A grey variety and a white variety also existed and the Grey Back (Saddleback) may have come from a cross. In contrast, the Asiatic geese such as the 'African' and Chinese are descended from the wild swan goose which, in the brown variety, they closely resemble in colour.

The British Waterfowl Association classifies the following as wild geese: Canada, Egyptian and all other species of wild geese.

## Goose Points

| Breed | Carriage | Head / throat | Neck | Body | Legs / feet | Condition | Colour | Size |
|---|---|---|---|---|---|---|---|---|
| | | SHAPE [Type] | | | | Condition | Colour | Size |
| African | 15 | 15 | 5 | 20 | 5 | 10 | 10 | 20 |
| American Buff | 10 | 10 | 5 | 20 | 5 | 10 | 25 | 15 |
| Brecon Buff | 10 | 10 | 5 | 25 | 5 | 10 | 25 | 10 |
| Buff Back | 10 | 5 | 5 | 20 | 5 | 10 | 35 | 10 |
| Chinese | 20 | 20 | 10 | 10 | 5 | 10 | 15 | 10 |
| Embden | 12 | 12 | 10 | 20 | 6 | 10 | 10 | 20 |
| Pilgrim | 10 | 10 | 5 | 15 | 5 | 10 | 35 | 10 |
| Pomeranian | 10 | 5 | 5 | 20 | 5 | 10 | 35 | 10 |
| Roman | 15 | 10 | 10 | 25 | 5 | 10 | 10 | 15 |
| Sebastopol | 15 | 5 | 5 | 10 | 5 | 40• | 10 | 10 |
| Steinbacher | 20 | 15 | 5 | 10 | 5 | 10 | 25 | 10 |
| Toulouse | 15 | 15 | 5 | 20 | 5 | 10 | 10 | 20 |
| West of England | 10 | 5 | 5 | 20 | 5 | 10 | 35 | 10 |

• Feather and condition

# Goose Morphology

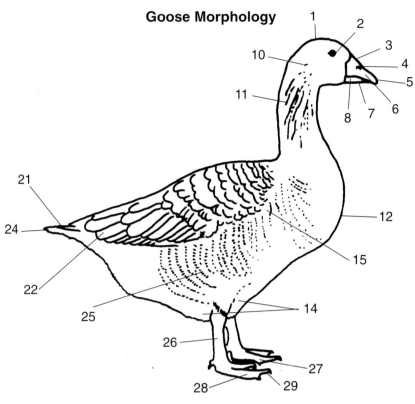

| | | |
|---|---|---|
| 1 crown | 11 neck-feather partings | 21 primaries |
| 2 eye | 12 breast | 22 secondaries |
| 3 culmen | 13 keel | 23 tertials |
| 4 nostril | 14 paunch or abdomen | 24 tail feathers |
| 5 bean (or nail) | 15 wing butt or front | 25 thigh coverts |
| 6 upper mandible | 16 scapular feathers | 26 shanks |
| 7 lower mandible | 17 primary coverts | 27 webs |
| 8 serrations | 18 greater coverts | 28 toes |
| 9 dewlap | 19 median coverts | 29 claw |
| 10 ear | 20 lesser coverts | |

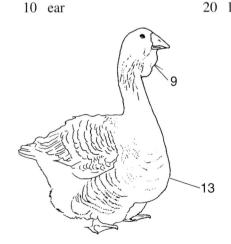

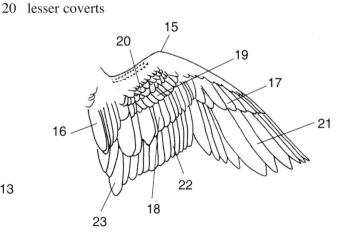

# AFRICAN

*Origin:* China
*Classification:* Heavy

The African is the large relative of the Chinese, having been developed from the wild swan goose which they both resemble.

## General characteristics: male and female

**Carriage:** Reasonably upright; body held at 30-40 degrees when active. Head held high and proud. Tail carried high, above the line of the back, especially in ganders.
**Head:** Broad, deep and large. Bill rather large and stout at the base. Knob large, as broad as the head and forwardly inclined, protruding from the front of the skull at the upper mandible (this feature naturally larger in ganders than geese). Eyes large. The lower jaw and upper neck carry a large dewlap which is regularly curved in a smooth crescent shape.
**Neck:** Long, massive, nearly the same thickness along its length. Gracefully but moderately arched.
**Body:** Large, long and nearly the same thickness from shoulders to stern. Back broad, moderately long and flat. Breast full and well rounded. Underline smooth and free from keel. If the paunch is not 'clean', there should be small, even dual lobes. Wings large and powerful, neatly folded against the sides of the body. Stern round and full, free from bagginess.
**Legs and feet:** Lower thighs short, stout. Shanks of medium length.
**Plumage:** Tight and sleek on the body. The neck plumage is smooth, like velvet (unlike the European breeds where the feathers are furrowed).

## Colour
### The Brown or Grey
*In both sexes*
*Head, neck and breast:* Lower part of head, front of neck, breast and underbody light fawn, fading to cream on the dewlap and throat. The breast shows a pinkish blush to the fawn. In contrast, a brown stripe extends from the crown down the back of neck. A faint, darker line also extends along the line of the jaw along the face. In most mature specimens a narrow band of white feathers surrounds the bill where it joins the head.
*Body:* Sides of body and thigh coverts ashy brown, each feather edged with a lighter shade. Feathers more strongly marked on the thigh coverts where there is a distinct white edging on the upper side tucked up to the wings. Back ashy brown. Underbody fawn fades to white on the stern.
*Tail:* Ashy brown heavily edged with near white. Tail coverts white.
*Wings:* Primaries and secondaries dark slate. Primary coverts light slate. Other large coverts light ashy brown, laced with a lighter shade. Scapulars ashy brown with light edging.
*Bill and knob:* Black. *Eyes:* Dark brown. *Legs and webs:* Dark orange or brownish orange. *Toe-nails:* Dark.

13

*African*

## The Buff
*In both sexes*
*Plumage:* Marked as in the brown; a dilute of the darker colour. Buff with creamy fawn on the lighter parts.
*Bill and knob:* Pinkish brown. *Legs and webs:* Dull light orange.

## The White
*In both sexes*
*Plumage:* Pure white.
*Bill and knob:* Orange. *Legs and webs:* Orange-yellow. *Eyes:* Blue.

## Weights:
| | | |
|---|---|---|
| Gander | 10.0-12.7kg | (22-28lb) |
| Goose | 8.2-10.9kg | (18-24lb) |

## Scale of points
| | |
|---|---|
| Carriage | 15 |
| Head and throat | 15 |
| Neck | 5 |
| Body | 20 |
| Legs and feet | 5 |
| Condition | 10 |
| Colour | 10 |
| Size | 20 |
| | **100** |

## Defects
Inadequate development of dewlap and knob. Refined head and neck indicative of Chinese type. Short body. Lack of reach. Keel on breast or underbody. Baggy paunch. Low tail carriage. Orange in knob or bill of the brown. Indication of white feathers in coloured plumage.

## Disqualifications
Undershot mandible. Excessive white feathers in the coloured plumage, except where described.

# AMERICAN BUFF

*Origin:* America
*Classification:* Heavy

The American Buff goose is a heavy breed with a stance like the Embden, smooth breasted and dual-lobed.

## General Characteristics: male and female

**Carriage:** Reasonably upright.
**Head:** Broad, oval, strong. Stout bill of medium length. Eyes large and full.
**Neck:** Rather upright and strong in appearance.
**Body:** Moderately long, broad, plump. Breast broad, deep and full. Dual-lobed paunch. Back medium in length, broad and smooth. Tail medium in length with broad stiff feathers. Wings medium in size and smoothly folded close to the body.
**Legs and feet:** Lower thighs medium length, well fleshed. Shanks stout, straight, moderately long.

## Colour

*In both sexes*
*Plumage:* A rich shade of orange-buff throughout with markings similar to the Toulouse.
*Bill:* Orange. *Eyes:* Dark hazel. *Legs and webs:* Orange.

## Weights

| | | |
|---|---|---|
| Gander | 10.0-12.7kg | (22-28lb) |
| Goose | 9.1-11.8kg | (20-26lb) |

## Scale of points

| | |
|---|---|
| Carriage | 10 |
| Head and throat | 10 |
| Neck | 5 |
| Body | 20 |
| Legs and feet | 5 |
| Condition | 10 |
| Colour | 25 |
| Size | 15 |
| | **100** |

## Defects

White feathers in coloured plumage (i.e. white flights and under chin) excepting white around the bill with age. Uneven lobes back and front.

*American Buff*

# BRECON BUFF

*Origin:* Great Britain
*Classification:* Medium

At different times attempts have been made to create a buff goose, and to Wales goes the credit of originating the Brecon Buff. This breed was founded on stock from Breconshire hill farms and was recognized officially in 1934. It is an active, hardy breed, with high flesh to bone ratio.

## General Characteristics: male and female

**Carriage:** Slightly upright, alert and active.
**Head:** Neat, no sign of coarseness. Bill medium length, strong, deep at the base. Eyes bright.
**Neck:** Medium in length, the throat showing no gullet.
**Body:** Broad, well rounded and compact. Breast full and round. Dual-lobed paunch. Wings strong.
**Legs and feet:** Legs fairly short. Strong shanks.
**Plumage:** Hard and tight.

## Colour

*In both sexes*
*Plumage:* A deep shade of buff throughout with markings similar to the Toulouse. Ganders are usually not as deeply coloured as the geese.
*Bill:* Pink. *Eyes:* Dark brown. *Legs and webs:* Pink.

## Weights

| | | |
|---|---|---|
| Gander | 7.3-9.1kg | (16-20lb) |
| Goose | 6.3-8.2kg | (14-18lb) |

## Scale of points

| | |
|---|---|
| Carriage | 10 |
| Head and throat | 10 |
| Neck | 5 |
| Body | 25 |
| Legs and feet | 5 |
| Condition | 10 |
| Colour | 25 |
| Size | 10 |
| | **100** |

## Defects

White feathers in the coloured plumage (i.e. white flights and under chin) except for around the upper bill with age. Bill, legs and feet not a clear pink. Uneven lobes on the paunch.

## Disqualifications

Orange beak or legs and feet. Excessive white feathers.

*Brecon Buff goose*

# BUFF BACK

*Origin:* Europe
*Classification:* Medium

## General characteristics: male and female
**Carriage:** Nearly horizontal.
**Head:** Fairly broad. Bill medium in length, stout and nearly straight.
**Neck:** Medium in length, moderately stout and carried upright with little or no indication of an arch.
**Body:** Moderately long, plump, deep and meaty with no evidence of a keel. Paunch moderately broad, deep and dual-lobed. Wings rather long with the tips crossing over the tail coverts. Tail closely folded and carried nearly level.
**Legs and feet:** Lower thighs medium length, plump. Shanks moderately long, sturdy.

## Colour
*In both sexes*
*Head:* Buff. Solid coloured heads preferred to specimens with excessive white feathers around the base of the bill.
*Neck:* Upper part buff, lower part white.
*Breast and flanks:* White except for buff thigh coverts laced with white. In some specimens a band of buff extends under the abdomen running between the buff thigh coverts.
*Back:* Buff from a point above the scapulars to near the base of the tail. Heart-shaped saddle-back marking formed by the scapulars and adjacent coverts.
*Tail:* Mainly white with some buff.
Wings: Primaries, secondaries and tertials white. Coverts mainly white.
*Bill:* Orange. *Eyes:* Blue. *Legs and webs:* Orange.

## Weights
| | | |
|---|---|---|
| Gander | 8.2-10.0kg | (18-22lb) |
| Goose | 7.3-9.1kg | (16-20lb) |

## Scale of points
| | |
|---|---|
| Carriage | 10 |
| Head and throat | 5 |
| Neck | 5 |
| Body | 20 |
| Legs and feet | 5 |
| Condition | 10 |
| Colour and markings | 35 |
| Size | 10 |
| | **100** |

## Defects
Uneven markings.

*Buff Back gander*

# CHINESE

*Origin:* China
*Classification:* Light

A prolific breed of the smaller bodied type of goose.

## General characteristics: male and female

**Carriage:** Upright, body held at about 45 degrees when active. Ganders especially should stand with their heads and tails held high.

**Head:** Medium in size. Bill stout at base, medium for size. Knob large, rounded and prominent (smaller in the goose than the gander). Eyes bold.

**Neck:** Long and refined, carried upright with graceful arch (longer in the gander than the goose).

**Body:** Compact and plump. Back reasonably short, broad, flat and sloping to give a characteristic upright carriage. Breast well rounded and plump, carried high. No double lobes on the abdomen; single central lobe occurs in laying geese. Wings large, strong and high up, carried closely. Stern well rounded. Tail carried high in exhibition strain birds where the wing tips cross over in front of the tail.

**Legs and feet:** Legs medium length. Shanks strong.

**Plumage:** Tight, sleek and firm.

## Colour

**The Brown or Grey**

*In both sexes*

*Head, neck and breast:* Lower part of head, front of neck, breast and underbody light fawn, fading to cream on the throat. In contrast a dark brown stripe extends from the crown down the back of the neck. A faint, darker line also extends along the line of the jaw along the face. In most mature specimens a narrow band of white feathers surrounds the bill where it joins the head.

*Body:* Sides of body and thigh coverts ashy brown, each feather edged with a lighter shade. Feathers more strongly marked on the thigh coverts where there is a distinct white edging on the upper side tucked up to the wings. Back ashy brown. Underbody fawn fades to white on the stern.

*Tail:* Ashy brown edged with near white. Tail coverts white.

*Wings:* Primaries and secondaries dark slate. Primary coverts light slate. Other large coverts light ashy brown, laced with a lighter shade. Scapulars ashy brown with light edging.

*Bill and knob:* Black. *Eyes:* Dark brown. *Legs and webs:* Dull orange or pinkish orange, feet often flecked with dark markings. *Toe-nails:* Dark

**The White**

*In both sexes*

*Plumage:* Pure white.

*Bill and knob:* Orange. *Eyes:* Blue. *Legs and webs:* Orange-yellow

*Brown Chinese gander*

*Embden Gander*

## Weights

| | | |
|---|---|---|
| Gander | 4.5-5.4kg | (10-12lb) |
| Goose | 3.6-4.5kg | (8-10lb) |

## Scale of points

| | |
|---|---|
| Carriage | 20 |
| Head and throat | 20 |
| Neck | 10 |
| Body | 10 |
| Legs and feet | 5 |
| Condition | 10 |
| Colour | 15 |
| Size | 10 |
| | **100** |

## Defects

Absence of knob. Any sign of a gullet. White in coloured plumage, except where specified.
Orange in the knob of brown variety. Coarseness or excessive weight.
Baggy undercarriage.

# EMBDEN

*Origin:* North Europe
*Classification:* Heavy

As the Embden breed was also known originally as the Bremen, one associates it with
Germany, although stock once reached us from Holland. In Germany and North Holland,
no doubt, they crossed the Italian white with their native whites, creating the Embden.
When stock did reach this country our breeders crossed the birds with English whites and
by careful selection increased the body weight and quantity of meat, while standardizing
the breed for its characteristics.

## General characteristics: male and female

**Carriage:** Upright and confident.
**Head:** Strong, bold. Stout bill. Eyes bold.
**Neck:** Long, well proportioned, without a gullet.
**Body:** Broad, thick and well rounded. Back long and straight. Breast round. Shoulders and
stern broad. Paunch deep and dual-lobed. Wings large and strong. Tail close and carried
well out.
**Legs and feet:** Legs medium length. Shanks large and strong.
**Plumage:** Hard and tight

## Colour

*In both sexes*
*Plumage:* Pure glossy white.
*Bill:* Orange. *Eyes:* Light blue. *Legs and webs:* Bright orange.

## Weights

| | | |
|---|---|---|
| Gander | 12.7-15.4kg | (28-34lb) |
| Goose | 10.9-12.7kg | (24-28lb) |

## Scale of points

| | |
|---|---|
| Carriage | 12 |
| Head and throat | 12 |
| Neck | 10 |
| Body | 20 |
| Legs and feet | 6 |
| Condition | 10 |
| Colour | 10 |
| Size | 20 |
| | **100** |

## Defects

Plumage other than white. Uneven lobes. Indication of a keel.

# GREY BACK

*Origin:* Northern Europe
*Classification:* Medium

The Grey Back is a commonly occurring colour type from the countries bordering the Baltic and the North Sea. In Britain it is similar in shape and markings to the Buff Back and, unlike the grey-back Pomeranian, it is dual-lobed in the paunch.

# PILGRIM

*Origin:* Great Britain. First standardized in the USA.
*Classification:* Light

Like the West of England, this breed is also auto-sexing. In Victorian times the ganders of the common goose were described as usually white while the geese were various shades of ash grey. The Pilgrim is believed to have been developed from this farmyard stock.

## General characteristics: male and female

**Carriage:** Above the horizontal, but not upright .
**Head:** Medium in size, oval, trim. Bill medium in length, straight, stout, smoothly attached. Eyes moderately large .
**Neck:** Medium in length, moderately stout, slightly arched.
**Body:** Moderately long, plump and meaty. Adult abdomen deep, dual-lobed and well balanced, free from bagginess. Back moderately broad, uniform in width, flat and straight. Breast round, full, deep. Wings strong, well developed, neatly carried to the body. Tail medium in length, closely folded, carried nearly level.

*Pilgrim goose and gander*

27

**Legs and feet:** Lower thighs medium in length, well fleshed. Shanks moderately short and stout.

**Plumage:** Hard, tight and glossy.

## Colour

*Gander*

*Plumage:* White. Some hidden light grey permissible in back plumage and in wings and tail.

*Goose*

*Head:* Light grey, the forepart broken with white and forming characteristic 'spectacles' around the eyes. White becoming more extensive with age.

*Neck:* Light grey, upper portion mixed with white in mature specimens.

*Breast:* Very light ashy grey, gradually getting lighter under the body. The stern is white.

*Flanks:* Soft, ashy grey, each feather edged with lighter shade.

*Back:* Light ashy grey, laced with lighter grey.

*Tail:* Ashy grey, heavily edged with a lighter grey approaching white.

*Wings:* Primaries medium grey; secondaries darker. Scapulars, greater and median coverts medium grey tipped with lighter grey. Lesser coverts light ashy grey, edged with lighter grey.

*In both sexes*

*Bill:* Orange. *Eyes:* Bluish grey in gander, hazel brown in goose.

*Legs and webs:* Orange.

## Weights

| | | |
|---|---|---|
| Gander | 6.3-8.2kg | (14-18lb) |
| Goose | 5.4-7.3kg | (12-16lb) |

## Scale of points

| | |
|---|---|
| Carriage | 10 |
| Head and throat | 10 |
| Neck | 5 |
| Body | 15 |
| Legs and feet | 5 |
| Condition | 10 |
| Colour | 35 |
| Size | 10 |
| | **100** |

## Defects

*In both sexes:* Flesh- or pink-coloured bills, feet and shanks. Single-lobed or unbalanced paunch. Undersize.

*In the gander:* Solid grey features in the plumage.

*In the goose:* White flights; all white heads; white blaze (on the breast). Predominantly white neck in the female to be subject to severe discrimination.

# POMERANIAN

*Origin:* Europe
*Classification:* Medium

## General characteristics: male and female
**Carriage:** Nearly horizontal
**Head:** Fairly broad, crown somewhat flat. Bill medium length, stout and nearly straight. Eyes large and prominent.
**Neck:** Medium in length, stout and carried upright. Thickness maintained along its length.
**Body:** Moderately long, plump, deep and meaty. Paunch moderately broad, deep, single-lobed. Breast plump and broad. Wings long with tips crossing over tail coverts, carried high, neatly and smoothly folded. Tail short, closely folded and carried nearly level.
**Legs and feet:** Lower thighs medium length, plump and nearly covered by ample thigh coverts. Shanks moderately long

## Colour
*In both sexes*
*Head:* Dark grey. Solid coloured heads preferred to specimens with white feathers around the base of the bill
*Neck:* Upper part dark grey, lower part white.
*Breast and flanks:* White except for grey thigh coverts laced with white. In some specimens a band of grey extends under the abdomen running between the grey thigh coverts.
*Back:* Dark grey edged with grey-white from a point above the scapulars to near the base of the tail. Heart-shaped saddle-back marking formed by the scapulars and adjacent coverts.
*Tail:* Mainly white, with some grey.
*Wings:* Primaries, secondaries and tertials white. Coverts mainly white.
*Bill:* Reddish or orange pink. *Legs and webs:* Orange-red. *Eyes:* Blue.

## Other Colours
There is also a solid grey variety [eyes brown] and a solid white variety [eyes blue].

## Weights
| | | |
|---|---|---|
| Gander | 8.2-10.9kg | (18-24lb) |
| Goose | 7.3-9.1kg | (16-20lb) |

*Pomeranian gander*

*Roman goose*

## Scale of points

| | |
|---|---:|
| Carriage | 10 |
| Head and throat | 5 |
| Neck | 5 |
| Body | 20 |
| Legs and feet | 5 |
| Condition | 10 |
| Colour and markings | 35 |
| Size | 10 |
| | **100** |

## Defects

Keel on breast. Uneven markings.

## Disqualification

Dual-lobed paunch.

# ROMAN

*Origin:* Mediterranean
*Classification:* Light

One of the smaller breeds of goose, the Roman was introduced into England from Italy about 1903, and there were other importations at later dates. Earliest arrivals were often marked with grey on the back, but this colour fault was eliminated by selective matings for pure white.

## General characteristics: male and female

**Carriage:** Active, alert. Horizontal.
**Head:** Neat and well rounded. Face deep. Bill short and not coarse. Eyes bold.
**Neck:** Upright, medium length and without gullet.
**Body:** Compact and plump, deep and broad but also well balanced. Back wide and flat. Breast full, well rounded, somewhat low and without keel. Wings long, strong and high up and well tucked up to the tail line. Stern well rounded off, paunch not too pronounced, dual-lobed. Tail close and carried well out.
**Legs and feet:** Legs short, light boned, well apart.
**Plumage:** Sleek, tight and glossy.

## Colour

*In both sexes:*
*Plumage:* Glossy white.
*Bill:* Orange-pink. *Eyes:* Light blue. *Legs and webs:* Orange-pink.

**The Crested Roman**
A tuft of feathers on the crown begins just over the eyes and inclines backwards. The tuft is less exaggerated than in crested ducks.

## Weights

| Gander | 5.4-6.3kg | (12-14lb) |
|--------|-----------|-----------|
| Goose  | 4.5-5.4kg | (10-12lb) |

## Scale of points

| | |
|---|---|
| Carriage | 15 |
| Head and throat | 10 |
| Neck | 10 |
| Body | 25 |
| Legs and feet | 5 |
| Condition | 10 |
| Colour | 10 |
| Size | 15 |
| | **100** |

## Defects

Plumage other than white. Excessive weight, coarseness and oversize.

# SEBASTOPOL

*Origin :* Eastern Europe.
*Classification:* Light

The Sebastopol is one of the most unusual of the breeds of domestic geese. The long frizzled or spiralled feathers and the loose fluffed plumage make the Sebastopol a unique and attractive breed. The breed is primarily one for the exhibitor but is a moderate egg-layer and a fast grower and thus has merit as a utility goose.

## *The Frizzle*
## General Characteristics: male and female

**Carriage:** Horizontal.
**Head:** Neat; bill of medium length. Eyes large and prominent.
**Neck:** Medium length and carried upright.
**Body:** Appears round because of the full feathering. Back medium length but appears short because the long feathers give the body a rounded ball appearance. Breast full and deep, lacking keel. Wing feathers long, well curled and flexible. They make the bird incapable of flight because they are devoid of stiff shafts. Tail composed of long, well curled feathers.
**Legs and feet:** Lower thighs short but stout, each covered with curled feathers. Shanks short and stout.
**Plumage:** Only feathers of head and upper neck smooth. Feathers on lower neck, breast and remainder of body profusely curled. Feathers covering wings and back should be long (the longer the better). Wing feathers well curled and free from stiff shafts. Specimens of good stock and in good condition should display back and wing feathers that almost touch the ground.

*Sebastopol*

## Colour
**The White**
*In both sexes*
*Plumage:* Pure white, though traces of grey in young females allowed.

**The Buff**
*In both sexes*
*Plumage:* Even buff interrupted by curled feathers.

## *The Smooth-breasted or Trailing-feather*
## General characteristics: male and female
**Carriage:** Horizontal.
**Head:** As the Frizzle.
**Neck:** As the Frizzle.
**Body:** Comparatively short. Back wide and rounded, sloping gently from shoulders to the tail. Breast smooth, full and rounded, without any keel. Paunch neat and smooth or dual-lobed, not heavy or sagging. Tail short and held closed, carried horizontally or a little elevated.
**Legs and feet:** Thighs short and strong. Shanks short and stout.
**Plumage:** The feathers of the head, neck, breast, belly and paunch are smooth. Feathers of the thigh coverts and flanks, scapulars and some wing coverts are broad and extended in length, profuse, loosely curled and spiralled; the long back feathers fall over the wings and rump often trailing along the ground. The shafts of the primaries and secondaries are soft and flexible. The barbs of these feathers are 'fluted' giving a slight wave to the edge of the vane. The tail is made up of unevenly set 'fluted' feathers. The plumage should obscure the legs and feet from view.

## Colour
As in the Frizzle.

*In both colours and types*
*Bill and webs:* Orange. *Eyes:* Bright blue in white Sebastopol; brown in the buff.

## Weights
| | | |
|---|---|---|
| Gander | 5.4-7.3kg | (12-16lb) |
| Goose | 4.5-6.3kg | (10-14lb) |

## Scale of points

| | |
|---|---|
| Carriage | 15 |
| Head and throat | 5 |
| Neck | 5 |
| Body | 10 |
| Legs and feet | 5 |
| Condition and feathering | 40 |
| Colour | 10 |
| Size | 10 |
| | **100** |

## Defects
Silky feathering on the back of the Frizzle. Angel wings in either variety.

# STEINBACHER

*Origin:* Area of Thuringia (in former East Germany)
*Classification:* Light

Bred from a cross of local and Chinese geese at the end of the last century. The breed was standardized (1932) in Germany in its original grey colour, then in the popular blue (1951).

## General characteristics: male and female
**Carriage:** Reasonably upright, proud stature.
**Head:** Neat, without knob or dewlap. Eyes large. Beak with straight or slightly convex culmen and black serration (tooth-like edge).
**Neck:** Medium length, strong, upright and straight.
**Body:** Slightly stocky. Back strong and wide, slightly sloping. Breast wide and full. No obvious paunch in young birds; in older birds a light, dual-lobed paunch acceptable. Wings long, tightly carried. Tail short, pointed and carried level.
**Legs and feet:** Thighs strong. Shanks strong, medium length.
**Plumage:** Smooth, flat.

## Colour
**The Blue**
*In both sexes*
*Plumage:* Light blue-grey colour to head, neck, breast, back, wings and thighs. The feathers of the shoulders, wings and thighs show sharp white but not too wide lacing. Tail feathers are grey with white lacing. Underbody and back silver blue.
*Bill:* Black bean at the tip and black serrations, the remainder bright orange, corresponding to the colour of the legs. *Eyes:* Dark brown, framed with a narrow yellow ring. *Legs and webs:* Bright orange.

**Other colours**
The grey variety is also standardized in Germany. Buff and cream varieties occur.

*Steinbacher gander*

## Weights

| | | |
|---|---|---|
| Gander | 6-7kg | (13-15lb) |
| Goose | 5-6kg | (11-13lb) |

## Scale of points

| | |
|---|---|
| Carriage | 20 |
| Head and throat | 15 |
| Neck | 5 |
| Body | 10 |
| Legs and feet | 5 |
| Condition | 10 |
| Colour | 25 |
| Size | 10 |
| | **100** |

## Defects

Body too heavy. Curved neck. Sign of knob or dewlap. Missing black bean on beak. Different beak or serration colour. Lacing absent. Leg colour other than bright orange.

# TOULOUSE

*Origin:* France
*Classification:* Heavy

The Toulouse was developed in France for table purposes. Stock was sent over to England and breeders crossed the birds with English Greys, developing the breed for body weight and quantity of flesh, as well as standard characteristics of plumage colour, markings and type.

## General characteristics male and female

**Carriage:** Nearly horizontal.
**Head:** Strong and massive. Bill strong, fairly short, slightly convex culmen. Eyes full.
**Neck:** Long and thick. A pendulous, well developed dewlap extends in folds from the base of the lower mandible down the upper neck.
**Body:** Long, broad and deep. Back slightly curved from the neck to the tail. Breast prominent, deep and full. On exhibition specimens, the keel on the breast is balanced by muscular supports either side which diverge along the lower ribs. This gives the fullness to the breast. Paunch and stern heavy, symmetrical and wide. Shoulders broad. Wings large and strong. Tail somewhat short, carried high and well spread.
**Legs and feet:** Legs short. Shanks stout and strong boned.
**Plumage:** Full and somewhat soft.

*Toulouse goose*

## Colour
**The Grey**
*In both sexes*
*Plumage:* Neck grey. Breast and keel rather light grey, shading darker to the thighs. Back, wings and thighs grey, each feather laced with an almost white edging, the flights without white. Stern, paunch and tail white, the tail with a broad band of grey across the centre. *Bill:* Orange. *Eyes:* Dark brown or hazel. *Legs and webs:* Deep reddish orange.

**The Buff**
This is identical to the grey in shape but the buff to replace the grey in colour requirements.
*Bill, legs and webs*: Orange. *Eyes:* Dark brown or hazel.

**The White**
*In both sexes*
*Plumage:* Pure white. *Bill, legs and webs:* Orange. *Eyes:* Blue.

## Weights
| | | |
|---|---|---|
| Gander | 11.8-13.6kg | (26-30lb) |
| Goose | 9.1-10.9kg | (20-24lb) |

## Scale of points
| | |
|---|---|
| Carriage | 15 |
| Head and throat | 15 |
| Neck | 5 |
| Body | 20 |
| Legs and feet | 5 |
| Condition | 10 |
| Colour | 10 |
| Size | 20 |
| | **100** |

## Defects
Cavities in front of the legs and paunch caused by lack of broad keel support; twisted keel. In coloured birds: white feathers in primaries or secondaries; white around the base of bill in young individuals. Slipped or cut wings. Dropped tongue.

# WEST OF ENGLAND

*Origin:* Europe
*Classification:* Medium

The principal feature of this breed is that it is auto-sexing.

## General characteristics: male and female
**Carriage:** Somewhat above the horizontal, but not upright.
**Head:** Neat, not coarse. Bill medium in length, straight and stout. Eyes moderately large.
**Neck:** Medium in length, moderately stout, slightly arched.
**Body:** Moderately long. Adult abdomen deep and well balanced. Paunch full and symmetrical, dual-lobed. Back broad, slightly convex. Wings long with tips crossing over the tail coverts. Tail medium in length, closely folded, carried nearly level.
**Legs and feet:** Thighs medium length, plump and nearly concealed by ample thigh coverts. shanks moderately long and rather refined, yet sturdy.
**Plumage:** Hard and tight.

## Colour
**Gander**
*Plumage:* Pure white.

**Goose**
*Plumage:* Mainly white.
*Head and neck:* Grey and white, the grey extending down the neck. Even grey marking preferred to dispersed blotches. White feathers may be mixed with the grey. Forepart of head white, becoming more extensive in older birds.
*Breast and flanks:* White. Thigh coverts grey, laced with white.
*Back:* Small centre back feathers grey.
*Tail:* Mainly white with grey in central feathers.
*Wings:* Primaries, secondaries and tertials white, the saddle-back being formed by the scapulars and coverts. Grey saddle-back feathers laced with white and in a symmetrical, clearly defined pattern.
*Bill:* Orange. *Eyes:* Blue. *Legs and webs:* Orange or pink.

## Weights

| | | |
|---|---|---|
| Gander | 7.3-9.1kg | (16-20lb) |
| Goose | 6.3-8.2kg | (14-18lb) |

## Scale of points

| | |
|---|---|
| Carriage | 10 |
| Head and throat | 5 |
| Neck | 5 |
| Body | 20 |
| Legs and feet | 5 |
| Condition | 10 |
| Colour | 35 |
| Size | 10 |
| | **100** |

## Defects

*In both sexes:* Undersize and very pink bill colour.

*In the goose:* Insufficient grey, especially in the head and neck; over-marking in the grey, extending onto the secondaries and spoiling the back marking.

# Other Breeds

The British Waterfowl Association looks after any other breeds of geese not standardized in this edition. Specimens of other breeds appear occasionally, but not so far in sufficient numbers to warrant standardizing.

### Shetland goose
This is a smaller variety of the West of England goose.

# Ducks

With the exception of the Muscovy, all domestic ducks are believed to be descendants of the various species, or sub-species, of mallard. This is quite obvious in the case of the Rouen and the Trout Indian Runner, both of which show typical elements of the mallard nuptial plumage. Each male has a 'hood' of iridescent green feathers that extends to a white ring half way down the neck. The breast feathers form a claret coloured 'bib' and the flanks show faint stippled pencilling. The females, however, retain a camouflage plumage all year round: most of the body feathers are a shade of brown with much darker brown pencilling towards the centre of the feather. Even in a wild population of **northern mallard**, *Anas p. platyrhynchos*, there is great variation in the shades of brown and the clarity of the pencilling. It is this inherent variability of the wild stock that has allowed human beings to select and develop the domestic breeds.

One remarkable characteristic of both male and female mallard is the iridescent blue secondary flights which form the 'mirror' or speculum, framed by lines of black and white that are reversed on the greater coverts. This feature is retained in many of the domestic breeds, although it is obscured in some cases by masking genes like the 'dusky factor' and various 'dilutions', in breeds such as the khaki Campbell and some Calls.

Whether *all* of the breeds, other than the Muscovy, are derived from the northern mallard is a matter for speculation. Certainly, in the wild, there are close relative species that will inter-breed with the mallard. One of the closest is the **Greenland mallard**, *Anas p. conboschas*, which looks very similar in colour to the Trout Indian Runner. Then there is the **American black duck**, *Anas rubripes*, which will hybridize with the mallard (Todd, 1979). This bird is a strong contender for ancestor of the Cayuga and the Black East Indian ducks, both of which were developed within the breeding range of *Anas rubripes*.

The original white ducks of Britain, on the other hand, are regarded as 'sports', mutations of the northern mallard, which is found in large numbers throughout Europe. It is a conveniently large bird and produces a range of variations. These have been considerably developed for body size and table qualities by domestication and selection, resulting in the Aylesbury as we know it today.

The British Waterfowl Association classifies the following as wildfowl: the Carolina, mandarin, and all other species of wild duck.

# Duck Points

| Breed | Carriage | Head etc | Body etc | Legs etc | Condition | Colour | Size |
|---|---|---|---|---|---|---|---|
| | | SHAPE [Type] | | | | | |
| Abacot Ranger | 10 | 15 | 15 | 5 | 10 | 35 | 10 |
| Aylesbury | 10 | 25 | 20 | 5 | 10 | 10 | 20 |
| Bali | 20 | ~30 | 15 | 5 | 10 | 10 | 10 |
| Black East Indian | 10 | 15 | 15 | 5 | 10 | 30 | 15 |
| Blue Swedish | 10 | 15 | 15 | 5 | 10 | 30 | 15 |
| Call | 10 | 20 | 20 | 5 | 10 | 20 | 15 |
| Campbell | 15 | 15 | 15 | 5 | 10 | 25 | 15 |
| Cayuga | 10 | 15 | 15 | 5 | 10 | 30 | 15 |
| Crested | 15 | *35 | 15 | 5 | 10 | 10 | 10 |
| Crested Miniature | 15 | #30 | 15 | 5 | 10 | 10 | 15 |
| Hook Bill | 15 | 25 | 15 | 5 | 10 | 20 | 10 |
| Indian Runner | 20 | 20 | 20 | 5 | 10 | 15 | 10 |
| Magpie | 10 | 15 | 15 | 5 | 10 | 35 | 10 |
| Muscovy | 10 | 20 | 15 | 5 | 10 | 20 | 20 |
| Orpington | 10 | 20 | 15 | 5 | 10 | 30 | 10 |
| Pekin | 20 | 20 | 15 | 5 | 10 | 10 | 20 |
| Rouen | 10 | 15 | 10 | 5 | 10 | 35 | 15 |
| Rouen Clair | 10 | 15 | 15 | 5 | 10 | 30 | 15 |
| Saxony | 10 | 15 | 15 | 5 | 10 | 30 | 15 |
| Silver Appleyard | 10 | 15 | 15 | 5 | 10 | 30 | 15 |
| Silver Appleyard Miniature | 10 | 15 | 15 | 5 | 10 | 30 | 15 |
| Silver Bantam | 10 | 15 | 15 | 5 | 10 | 30 | 15 |
| Welsh Harlequin | 10 | 15 | 15 | 5 | 10 | 35 | 10 |

* 25 points (out of 35 allocated for head etc.) are for the crest.
# 20 points (out of the 30 allocated for the head etc.) are for the crest.
~ 10 points (out of the 30 allocated for the head etc.) are for the crest.

# Duck Morphology

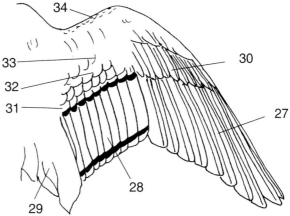

| | | |
|---|---|---|
| 1 crown | 10 nape | 19 upper tail coverts |
| 2 forehead | 11 shoulders | 20 tail feathers |
| 3 nostril | 12 neck | 21 sex feathers (in drake) |
| 4 upper mandible | 13 breast | 22 scapulars |
| 5 culmen | 14 underbody | 23 web |
| 6 bean or nail | 15 flanks | 24 toes |
| 7 lower mandible | 16 stern | 25 hind toe |
| 8 ear | 17 rump | 26 shank |
| 9 crest | 18 undertail | |

## Head

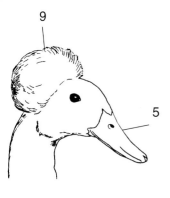

## Wing feathers

| | | |
|---|---|---|
| 27 primary feathers | 30 primary coverts | 33 lesser coverts |
| 28 secondary feathers (speculum) | 31 greater coverts | 34 marginal coverts |
| 29 tertials | 32 median coverts | |

# ABACOT RANGER

*Origin:* Great Britain
*Classification:* Light

The Abacot Ranger was developed primarily between 1917 and 1923 as a laying breed by Mr. Oscar Gray. Introduced into Germany in the early 1920s, a standard was drawn up in that decade for the Streicher duck that has not altered to the present day. A decorative and useful breed providing large white eggs and a good, well-flavoured carcass.

## General Characteristics: male and female

**Carriage:** Slightly erect, alert and busy; the drake a little more upright than the duck.
**Head:** Well rounded with a slightly raised brow. Bill medium length, rising in a gentle curve to the brow; should not be wedge-shaped.
**Neck:** Medium length, not too thin and only slightly curved, becoming thicker at the base and joining smoothly at the body.
**Body:** Longish, well rounded but not too full, and without any keel. The almost straight back runs approximately parallel to the underside. Wings carried somewhat high and held close to the body. Tail only slightly elevated.
**Legs and feet:** Legs medium length, longer in the drake than the duck. Set towards the stern, but not too far back and set well apart.
**Plumage:** Tight and glossy.

## Colour

### Drake

*Head and neck:* Brown-black overlaid with an intense green iridescence terminated above the shoulder by a completely encircling silver-white ring, dividing in a sharp clean line the neck and breast colours.
*Breast, neck base and shoulders:* Rich red-brown with silver-white lacing; the colour finishing in a line from the wing fronts.
*Flanks, underbody and stern:* Silvery white to cream (a white ground colour being preferable). A little of the breast colour washing along the upper flank permissible.
*Back:* Lower back dark grey with darker points, each feather laced with white. Rump brown-black with a slight iridescence, each feather lightly laced with white. Brown-black 'sex-curls' tipped with white.
*Tail:* Brownish black, the whole bordered with white. The lower tail covert brown-black, laced with white, finishing neatly and not running into the stern and flank colour.
*Wings:* Primaries silvery white with a slightly iridescent dark grey overlay. Secondaries (speculum) violet-green tipped with distinct black then white bars. Greater coverts tipped with distinct white and black.
Scapulars and tertials as the breast with wider silver-white lacing; smaller coverts French grey with a lighter edging.
*Bill:* Yellowish green with black bean at the tip. *Eyes:* Dark brown.
*Leg and webs:* Orange.

*Abacot Ranger  drake and duck*

*Duck*

*Head and neck:* Fawnish buff with the brow and crown strongly grained with dark brown (not black). The impression of a white neck ring is given in the sharp division between the neck and upper breast colour.

*Upper breast, lower neck and shoulders:* Lightly streaked with light brown on a pale cream ground.

*Flanks:* Lightly streaked.

*Lower breast, underbody and stern:* Creamy white.

*Lower back:* Light fawn with darker points and laced with light grey-brown. Rump fawnish grey with brown tips forming a triangular pattern.

*Tail:* Fawn, edged with cream.

*Wings:* Primaries and speculum as the drake. Scapulars and tertials creamy fawn with brown flecks. Smaller coverts dark fawn laced with cream.

The white ground colour in the bird to prevail.

*Bill:* Dark grey, almost black. *Eyes:* Dark brown. *Legs and webs:* As dark grey as possible.

### In both sexes

Under-down white.

## Weights

| | | |
|---|---|---|
| Drake | 2.5-2.7kg | ($5\frac{1}{2}$-6lb) |
| Duck | 2.3-2.5kg | (5-$5\frac{1}{2}$lb) |

## Scale of points

| | |
|---|---|
| Carriage | 10 |
| Head, bill and neck | 15 |
| Body | 15 |
| Legs and feet | 5 |
| Condition | 10 |
| Colour (ground 10, bill 5, feet 5, head 10, wings 5) | 35 |
| Size | 10 |
| | **100** |

## Defects

*In the drake:* Too dark a ground colour. Breast colour running too low into body. Lack of lacing. Lack of white tips on sex curls. Brown head. Broken, too wide or absent neck ring. Blue bill.

*In the duck:* Coarse or black graining and an eye stripe on the head. Absence of brown graining and streaking; white head. Yellow bill.

*In both sexes:* Absent or defective speculum and framing (black and white border). Keel on breast or underbody.

# AYLESBURY

*Origin:* Great Britain
*Classification:* Heavy

The Aylesbury derives its name from the town of Aylesbury in Buckinghamshire. At the first poultry show of 1845 a class was provided for 'Aylesbury or other white variety' and for 'Any other variety'. No doubt there were white ducks in this country for centuries before, and the Aylesbury was developed from them by judicious selection for table purposes. Once standardized as a breed it was developed by selecting for its distinctive characteristics, which separated it from all other white breeds of ducks.

## General characteristics: male and female
**Carriage:** Horizontal, the keel parallel with the ground.
**Head:** Strong and powerful, with eyes near the top of the skull. Bill long and broad. When viewed from the side the outline is almost straight from the top of the skull, the head and bill measuring from 15 to 20 cm (6 to 8 inches). Eyes full.
**Neck:** Average length, same width from head to breast, not thin.
**Body:** Long, broad and very deep. Back straight, sloping slightly from shoulders to tail. Breast full and prominent. Keel well defined, straight from breast to stern. Wings strong and carried closely to the sides, fairly high but not touching across the saddle. Tail short, only slightly elevated.
**Legs and feet:** Legs very strong, the bones thick, set to balance a level carriage.
**Plumage:** Bright and glossy, resembling satin.

## Colour
*In both sexes*
*Plumage:* White
*Bill:* Pink-white. *Eyes:* Blue. *Legs and webs*: Bright orange.

## Weights
| | | |
|---|---|---|
| Drake | 4.5-5.4kg | (10-12lb) |
| Duck | 4.1-5.0kg | (9-11lb) |

## Scale of points
| | |
|---|---|
| Carriage | 10 |
| Head, bill and neck | 25 |
| Body | 20 |
| Legs and feet | 5 |
| Condition | 10 |
| Colour | 10 |
| Size | 20 |
| | **100** |

## Defects
Plumage other than white. Bill other than pink-white or flesh pink.

*Aylesbury drake*

*Indian Fawn-and-white Runners - drake and duck; Bali drake.*

# BALI

*Origin:* East Indies
*Classification:* Light

Originally imported from Malaysia in 1925, these ducks take their name from Bali, an island east of Java where they are indigenous. The breed has recently been re-created in Britain by crossing crested ducks with Indian Runners, resulting in a crested Runner which has squarer shoulders than the exhibition white Runner. Crested Runners from Indonesia are also of this slightly heavier type of build.

## General characteristics: male and female
**Carriage:** Upright and active (as Indian Runner).
**Head:** Like the Indian Runner, except for a small, globular crest on the rear of the head.
**Neck:** Slim, fairly long, smoothly attached to the shoulders.
**Body:** Slightly heavier than the Indian Runner, but slim and cylindrical with not too much shoulder. Wings packed tight to the body.
**Legs and feet:** Legs strong, set well to the rear of the body to give the upright carriage.
**Plumage:** Tight and hard.

## Colour
**The white**
*In both sexes*
*Plumage:* Pure white throughout without any colour in the feathering
*Bill:* Orange-yellow. *Eyes:* Blue. *Legs and webs:* Orange.

**The coloured**
Any colour is permitted but attention should be paid to symmetry of markings.

## Weights
| | | |
|---|---|---|
| Drake | 2.3kg | (5lb) |
| Duck | 1.8kg | (4lb) |

## Scale of points
| | | |
|---|---|---|
| Carriage | 20 | |
| Head, bill and neck | 30 | [This includes ten points for the crest] |
| Body | 15 | |
| Legs and feet | 5 | |
| Condition | 10 | |
| Colour | 10 | |
| Size | 10 | |
| | **100** | |

## Defects
Domed head. Exaggerated crest. Low body station, thick shoulders or too heavy body reminiscent of the Crested.

*Black East Indian drake*

# BLACK EAST INDIAN

*Origin:* America
*Classification:* Bantam

The Black East Indian is described in the first book of standards in 1865, but it has had other names such as the Buenos Aires, Labrador and Black Brazilian. Many consider this is a black sport from the mallard.

## General Characteristics: male and female
**Carriage:** Lively and slightly elevated.
**Head:** Neat and round, with high skull. Bill medium length and fairly broad. Eyes full.
**Neck:** Medium length.
**Body:** Compact. Breast round and prominent .
**Legs and feet:** Legs medium length.
**Plumage:** Close, smooth and glossy.

## Colour
*In both sexes*
*Plumage:* Black with a lustrous beetle green sheen.
*Bill:* Black. *Eyes:* Dark brown. *Legs and webs:* As black as possible.

## Weights
| | | |
|---|---|---|
| Drake | 0.9kg | (2lb) |
| Duck | 0.7-0.8kg | $(1\frac{1}{2}-1\frac{3}{4}\text{lb})$ |

## Scale of points
| | |
|---|---|
| Carriage | 10 |
| Head, bill and neck | 15 |
| Body | 15 |
| Legs and feet | 5 |
| Condition | 10 |
| Colour | 30 |
| Size | 15 |
| | **100** |

## Defects
Purple sheen; brown or white in the plumage. Shallow or narrow boat-shaped body; pronounced rounded body as a Call duck. Over long bill; flattened bill with exaggerated serrations ('fish billed'). Green or yellow bill; grey tip on bill to be less severely penalized. Oversize.

# BLUE SWEDISH

*Origin:* Europe
*Classification:* Heavy

The Blue Swedish duck has long been admired for its striking appearance. Its rich, well-laced blue colour, large size, length and carriage, with the added bonus of two white flight feathers, make this bird a challenge for any breeder.

## General Characteristics: male and female

**Carriage:** From 20 to 25 degrees above the horizontal. Lively and alert.
**Head:** Oval, bold. Bill medium length. Eyes bright.
**Neck:** Average length, same width from head to breast, not thin.
**Legs and feet:** Legs medium length; set a little back from centre.
**Body:** Large, broad and deep without any suggestion of a keel. Breast full and round. Wings strong, compact and carried close to the body. Tail slightly elevated.

## Colour

*Head:* In the drake, dark blue with greenish lustre. In the duck, dark blue.
*In both sexes:* Body plumage a uniform shade of slate blue, strongly laced with a darker shade of this blue throughout except for an unbroken, inverted heart-shaped white 'bib' about 7.5 x 10cm [3 x 4in] in extent upon the lower neck and upper breast. Wings same as body colour, except that the two outer primaries in each should be white. Speculum as inconspicuous as possible
*Bill:* In the drake blue preferred to green. In the duck blue slate. *Eyes:* Brown.
*Legs and webs:* Orange-black in drake; blue-brown in the duck.

## Weights

| | | | | | |
|---|---|---|---|---|---|
| Adult drake | 3.6kg | (8lb) | adult duck | 3.2kg | (7lb) |
| Young drake | 3.2kg | (7lb) | young duck | 2.7kg | (6lb) |

## Scale of points

| | |
|---|---|
| Carriage | 10 |
| Head, bill and neck | 15 |
| Body | 15 |
| Legs and feet | 5 |
| Condition | 10 |
| Colour | 30 |
| Size | 15 |
| | **100** |

## Defects

Lack of size. Visible keel in either sex. White bib extending to lower mandible. Incorrect number of white primaries. Russet tinge, or black and green flecks in plumage. Indication of iridescent speculum.

*Blue Swedish drake*

# CALL

*Origin:* Possibly imported from Asia into Holland.
*Classification:* Call

First standardized in Great Britain. These birds were included in the first Standard of Excellence (1865) when the breed was known as the Decoy. Emphasis is placed upon alertness in looks and movements.

## General characteristics: male and female

**Carriage:** Nearly level from breast to stern
**Head:** Relatively large. Round, with a high crown, rising abruptly from the bill. Full cheeks. Bill broad and short, maximum length 3.1cm ($1\frac{1}{4}$ inches), set squarely in the head. Eyes large, round and alert.
**Neck:** Short and thick.
**Body:** Small and compact, broad and deep with a full breast. Tail carried almost level.
**Legs and feet:** Legs short, set midway in the body.

## Colour
**The Apricot**
This is considered to be a dilute of the mallard pattern, derived from the blue fawn.

### Drake
*Head and neck:* Silvery grey, white collar almost encircling the neck.
*Breast:* Mulberry with no white fringing; margin clearly defined.
*Flanks and underbody:* Very light grey feathers with apricot-grey stippling.
*Back:* Light grey feathers with darker edge, shading to blue-grey at the rump and undertail.
*Tail:* Light grey, central feathers darker than outer.
*Wings:* Primaries and coverts light pearl grey with apricot tinge, secondaries (speculum) darker pearl grey. Tertials grey, apricot tinge on outer part. Scapulars grey, edged with pale brown.
*Bill:* Light green, dark bean. *Eyes:* Brown.

### Duck
*Head and neck:* Apricot. Band of grey on crown; faint eye stripes as in the mallard Call.
*Breast and flanks:* Rich apricot. Underbody similar.
*Back:* Light grey feathers laced with apricot.
*Tail:* Apricot-grey.
*Wings:* Primaries light pearl grey, tinged with apricot. Secondaries (speculum) darker pearl grey. Coverts light grey laced with apricot. Scapulars grey, laced or tinged with apricot.
*Bill:* Light brown or with dark saddle. *Eyes:* Brown.

### In both sexes
*Legs and webs:* Orange.

*Call Ducks - Top, Apricot drake and duck*
*Bottom, Blue Fawn drake and duck*

*Call Ducks - Top left, Black and Blue Bibbed ducks*
*Top right, Magpie drake*
*Bottom, Pied drake and duck*

*In both sexes:* White primaries.
*In the drake:* Yellow bill, mulberry flank feathers, white fringing on the bib feathers.
*In the duck:* Presence of neck ring, lack of eye stripes.

## The Bibbed
*Colour in both sexes*
*Bodies and heads:* black, blue or lavender with white bibs. Green lustre on head of drake.
*Bib:* As even as possible, ideally an inverted heart shape extending from the lower neck to the upper breast.
*Tail:* Same colour as body, or slightly paler in blue or lavender
*Wings:* White in outer primaries. Bibbed follows Blue Swedish for colour: two white outer feathers preferred.
*Bill:* Olive in the drake, in the duck black.
*Legs and webs:* Dusky orange shaded irregularly with greyish black.

*Colour defects*
Uneven or large bib extending around the bill; ragged edges to the bib; white line through the eye. Russet tinge in the plumage.

## The Blue Fawn
This is considered to be a dilute of the mallard i.e. it has the same pattern in a paler colour.

*Drake*
*Head and neck:* Charcoal blue with white collar almost encircling the neck.
*Breast:* Claret with no white fringing; margin clearly defined.
*Flanks and underbody:* Light grey with grey stippling.
*Back:* Body feathers blue-grey shading to dark blue-grey at the rump and undertail.
*Tail:* Darker blue-grey in the centre, paler outer feathers
*Wings:* Primaries smoke grey, secondaries (speculum) matt charcoal blue. Tertials blue-grey, bronze on the outer part. Coverts blue-grey. Scapulars smoke grey, darker at outer edge.
*Bill:* Green, dark bean. *Eyes:* Brown.

*Duck*
*Head and neck:* Darker band of blue-grey on crown and neck; distinct fawn graining on the crown. Eye stripes as in the mallard, pale fawn throat.
*Breast and flanks:* Fawn, each feather flecked or pencilled with blue-grey. Underbody similar.
*Back:* Mainly blue with distinct but fine fawn lace, becoming finer on the larger feathers.
*Tail:* Blue-grey with fawn tinge; paler outer feathers.
*Wings:* Primaries and secondaries as drake. Coverts blue-grey. Scapulars as back.
*Bill:* Brown or with dark saddle, variable in extent. *Eyes:* Brown.

*In both sexes*
*Legs and webs:* Orange, slightly darker webs in the duck.

*White Call drake*

*Colour defects*
*In both sexes:* White primaries.
*In the drake:* Claret flank feathers or white fringing on the bib feathers; absence of neck ring.
*In the duck:* Broad fawn lacing detracting from blue back feathers; lack of eye stripes.

## The Dark Silver
*Drake*
A darker version of the silver. Breast and flank feathers a more solid claret; less white fringing.
Lower flanks grey; underbody grey or grey mixed with white.

### Duck
*Head and neck:* Fawn with darker grey-brown graining. Faint light buff eye stripes. Paler plain throat.
*Breast, flanks and back:* Feathers fawn with darker grey-brown pencilling on each feather.
*Underbody:* Cream with finer dark brown flecking.
*Tail:* Upper and undercoverts brown with cream edging.
*Wings:* Primaries creamy fawn to dark brown. Speculum and borders as drake. Tertials mottled brown. Coverts light brown with cream. Scapulars as flanks and back.
*Bill:* Dark orange with brown saddle. *Eyes:* Brown.

### In both sexes
*Legs and webs:* Orange

*Colour defects*
Pied markings in the head, or clear white primaries.

## The Magpie
### In both sexes
*Colour and markings:* As for the large Magpie ducks.
*Legs and webs:* Dusky orange shaded irregularly with greyish black

*Colour defects*
Plumage defects as large Magpie. Lacing on black plumage. Body more than 50% black, or more than 80% white.

## The Mallard (also known as Brown or Grey)
*Drake*
*Head and neck:* Iridescent green with distinct white collar almost encircling the neck.
*Breast:* Rich claret with no white fringing; margin of claret clearly defined.
*Flanks and underbody:* Light grey with dark grey stippling.
*Back:* Dark grey shading to greenish black over the rump and undertail.
*Tail:* Medium dull brown, paler outer feathers; coverts black.
*Wings:* Primaries and tertials grey; speculum blue bordered by black then white. Coverts brownish grey except for greater coverts which are tipped with white then black. Main scapulars clear steel grey, outer edge bronze tinge.
*Bill:* Green, dark bean. *Eyes:* Dark brown.

### Duck

*Head and neck:* Golden brown, each feather with darker brown graining; slight green sheen on black graining on the crown. This graining forms a darker band from the crown down the back of the neck. Eye stripes as in the wild mallard. Plain brown throat.
*Breast and flanks:* Brown or chestnut with dark brown pencilling on each feather. Underbody similar.
*Back:* Brown or chestnut with darker pencilling.
*Tail:* Dull dark buff, irregularly marked with brown; darker tail feathers in the centre than the outer edges.
*Wings:* Primaries brownish slate, speculum and its borders as drake. Tertials browner than primaries on exposed half. Coverts and scapulars same colour as back.
*Bill:* Dark orange with brown saddle. *Eyes:* Brown.

### In both sexes

*Legs:* Dull orange, darker webs.

### Colour defects

*In both sexes:* White primaries, white feathers under the bill, on the throat and under the tail or very pale outer tail feathers.
*In the drake:* Absence of neck ring; white fringing on the bib feathers. Black marks on drake's bill a minor defect.
*In the duck:* Dark ground colour and lack of pencilling in back feathers. Presence of white collar. Lack of eye stripes.

## The Pied

Coloured feathers basically as mallard Call. Variations on pied markings allowed i.e. amount of white on the flanks, primaries, tail and neck compared with the brown. Symmetrical markings preferred.

### Drake

*Head and neck:* Green, sometimes with white feathers surrounding the base of bill. A white line starts at rear of eyes and encircles the back of head. A wide white ring encircles the neck. Extent of white markings on head variable.
*Body:* Colour basically as mallard except underside of body behind legs white.
*Tail:* Coloured or white feathers, number of each colour depending on amount of body colour.
*Wings:* Outer primaries white.
*Bill:* Light yellow with greenish tinge.

### Duck

*Head and neck:* White marking as drake
*Body:* White area often more extensive than the drake.
*Tail:* Colour variation as drake.
*Wings:* White can extend onto wing coverts and blue speculum may be lost.
*Bill:* Yellow with brown saddle.

*Call Ducks - Top, Mallard drake and duck*
        *Bottom, Dark Silver duck and drake*

## In both sexes
*Legs and webs*: Orange.

## Colour defects
Lack of blue speculum in duck a minor fault only. Asymmetry of markings and insufficiency of white to be more heavily penalized.

## The Silver
### Drake
*Head and neck:* As mallard but wider neck ring, completely encircling the neck.
*Breast:* Claret with each feather laced with white. Claret split by more white on the lower breast.
*Flanks:* Light claret feathers along the upper flank, each feather edged with white. Lower flanks and underbody white.
*Back:* Light grey with black frosting, shading to black with beetle green sheen on the rump.
*Tail:* Paler outer feathers; central feathers darker, each feather having a grey centre and paler off-white edging. Undertail black with green sheen.
*Wings:* Primaries off-white, marked with dark grey, more so on the outer edge and tip. Speculum blue with black then white band on the secondaries; bands missing from greater coverts. Tertials grey stipple with browner outer edge. Scapulars grey stipple; smaller scapulars claret outer edge.
*Bill:* Green, black bean. *Eyes:* Brown.

### Duck
*Head and neck:* Pale fawn to cream with darker graining on the crown. No eye stripes.
*Body:* White with brown and grey mottling, more pronounced on upper body and breast.
*Tail:* White outer feathers, central feathers grey mottled.
*Wings:* Primary feathers almost white, dark stippling on the outer tips and edges. Speculum as drake. Tertials carry more colour than flights.
*Bill:* Light orange-brown with rich brown saddle. *Eyes:* Brown.

## In both sexes
*Legs and webs:* Orange.

## Colour defects
*In both sexes:* Lack of speculum; clear white primaries.
*In the drake:* Pied markings in the head and light streaks in the undertail.
*In the duck:* Buff ground colour pencilled with brown.

## The White
### In both sexes
*Plumage:* Pure white.
*Bill:* Bright orange-yellow. *Eyes:* Leaden blue (appear dark). *Legs and webs:* Bright orange.

*Colour Defects*
Any black in the drake's bill is a disqualification.
Black specks on the duck's bill are a common minor fault with age.

## Weights

| | | |
|---|---|---|
| Drake | 0.6-0.7kg | $(1\frac{1}{4}-1\frac{1}{2}$lb) |
| Duck | 0.5-0.6kg | $(1-1\frac{1}{4}$lb) |

## Scale of points

| | |
|---|---|
| Carriage | 10 |
| Head, bill and neck | 20 |
| Body | 20 |
| Legs and feet | 5 |
| Condition | 10 |
| Colour | 20 |
| Size | 15 |
| | **100** |

## Defects
Thin-bodied, boat-shaped body. Legs positioned too far back causing breast to tip. Long, slim neck. Flat crown, oval head or square head showing a flat top. Narrow cheeks, uneven cheeks e.g. from sinus infection. Long, narrow bill. Oversize. Long shanks.

# CAMPBELL

*Origin:* Great Britain
*Classification:* Light

The wild mallard played a part in the make up of the khaki Campbell, together with the fawn-and-white Runner and the Rouen. Introduced in 1901 by Mrs Campbell of Uley, Gloucestershire, it was her special desire to keep the breed for prolific egg-laying, so that only a very elementary standard was at first publicized. In this way the egg-laying properties of the breed were maintained. The white Campbell came as a sport from the khaki. The dark Campbell was created by Mr. H.R.S.Humphreys in Devon, to make sex-linkage in ducks possible.

## General characteristics: male and female
**Carriage:** Alert, slightly upright, the head carried high. Shoulders higher than the saddle, the back showing a gentle slant. Carriage not too erect (about 35 degrees) but not so low as to cause waddling. Activity and foraging power to be retained without loss of body depth and width.
**Head:** Refined in jaw and skull; neat boned with smooth face. Bill medium length, depth and width; set in a straight line with the top of the skull. Eyes full, bold and bright, fairly high in skull and prominent.
**Neck:** Medium length, slender, almost erect.

**Body:** Deep, wide and compact. Breast broad and well rounded. Back wide, flat and of medium length. Abdomen well developed but not sagging; well rounded underline from breast to stern. Wings carried closely and rather high. Tail short and small, slightly elevated.

**Legs ands feet:** Legs medium length, set well apart and not too far back.

**Plumage:** Tight and sleek.

## Colour
### The Dark
### Drake
*Head and neck:* Beetle green.

*Shoulders, breast, underbody and flanks:* Light brown, each feather finely stippled (pencilled) with dark grey-brown, gradually shading to grey at the stern close up to the vent.

*Rump:* Beetle green.

*Tail:* Dark grey-brown. Tail coverts beetle green with purplish tinge .

*Wings:* Primaries dark brown. Speculum purplish green, edged with a thin light grey line on each side. Coverts dark grey-brown laced with light brown.

*Bill:* Bluish green with black bean. *Eyes:* Brown. *Legs and webs:* Bright orange.

### Duck
*Head and neck:* Dark brown.

*Shoulders, breast and flank:* Light brown, each feather broadly pencilled with dark brown, becoming brown towards the stern, with lighter outer lacing.

*Back:* Dark brown; rump beetle green.

*Tail:* Dark brown.

*Wings:* Primaries dark brown; speculum as drake, but less lustrous. Smaller coverts laced with lighter brown.

*Bill:* Slaty brown with black bean. *Eyes:* Brown. *Legs and webs:* As near body colour as possible.

### Colour defects
Yellow bill. White bib or neck ring.

### The Khaki
### Drake
*Head, neck, rump, and secondaries (speculum):* Green-bronze.

Remainder of plumage an even shade of warm khaki shading to lighter khaki towards the lower part of the breast.

*Bill:* Greenish blue, the darker the better. *Legs and webs:* Dark orange. *Eyes:* Brown.

### Duck
An even shade of warm khaki.

*Head and neck:* A slightly darker shade.

*Breast:* Lightly pencilled, on close inspection.

*Back and scapulars:* pencilled.

*Khaki Campbell duck and drake*

*Wings:* Khaki, top and under. Secondaries brown.
*Bill:* Dark slate. *Eyes:* Brown. *Legs and webs:* As near the body colour as possible.

### Colour defects
*In both sexes:* Yellow bill. White bib or neck ring. White or light underpart or top of wings. White in secondaries.
*In the duck:* Mallard face markings (light streak above the eye, dark line through the eye); lack of pencilling on breast and back; heavy pencilling as in the Rouen.

### The White
### In both sexes
*Plumage:* Pure white throughout.
*Bill, legs and webs:* Orange. *Eyes:* Grey-blue.
### Colour defects
Flesh coloured bill. Dark markings on the bill. Coloured feathers.

## Weights
Drake   2.3-2.5kg   (5-5$\frac{1}{2}$lb)
Duck in laying condition   2.0-2.2kg   (4$\frac{1}{2}$-5lb)

## Scale of points
| | |
|---|---|
| Carriage | 15 |
| Head, bill and neck | 15 |
| Body | 15 |
| Legs and feet | 5 |
| Condition | 10 |
| Colour | 25 |
| Size | 15 |
| | **100** |

## Defects
Excessive weight or coarseness. Flesh-coloured bill.

# CAYUGA

*Origin:* America
*Classification:* Heavy
This breed takes its name from Lake Cayuga in New York State. It was in the early 1850s when large black ducks made an appearance on the lake. Present-day Cayugas are thought to be descended from these. Black East Indians were said to have been used to improve the colour in these birds

## General characteristics: male and female
**Carriage:** Nearly horizontal, clear of the ground from breast to stern.
**Head:** Large; bill long and wide. Eyes full and bold.
**Neck:** Long and strong with a graceful curve.

*Cayuga duck*

*Crested duck*

**Body**: Long, broad and deep; breast broad, full and prominent; clean underline. Tail long and closely folded; slightly elevated.

**Legs and feet:** Legs placed midway in the body giving the bird only a slightly elevated carriage.

**Plumage:** Smooth, close and glossy.

## Colour

*In both sexes*

*Plumage:* Black with a lustrous beetle green sheen.

*Bill:* Black. *Eyes:* Dark brown. *Legs and webs:* As black as possible.

## Weights

| | | |
|---|---|---|
| Drake | 3.6kg | (8lb) |
| Duck | 3.2kg | (7lb) |

## Scale of points

| | |
|---|---|
| Carriage | 10 |
| Head, bill and neck | 15 |
| Body | 15 |
| Legs and feet | 5 |
| Condition | 10 |
| Colour | 30 |
| Size | 15 |
| | **100** |

## Defects

Purple lustre, brown or white in the plumage. Yellow or green bill; grey tip on bill to be less severely penalized. Indication of keel on breast or undercarriage. Orange in legs,
especially females.

# CRESTED

*Origin:* Not really known

*Classification:* Light

Some publications state that it originated in Britain, whilst others think that Holland was the country of origin, as old Dutch paintings (1660) feature crested ducks. Whichever is correct, crested ducks are a challenge in themselves for the breeder.

## General characteristics: male and female

**Carriage:** Reasonably upright when active, at approximately 35 to 40 degrees.

**Head:** Long and straight, slightly rising to the crown, the centre of which has a well balanced, even, globular crest firmly attached to the skull. Bill long and broad. Eyes bright.

**Neck:** Average length and slightly curved.

**Legs and feet:** Legs medium length.

**Body:** Long, broad and moderately deep. Full, well rounded breast blending nicely into body. Wings strong, carried close to the body, usually just failing to meet over the rump. The overall picture of the bird, including the crest, is balance throughout. Tail in proportion to the bird and closed.

**Plumage:** Close and smooth.

## Colour

**The White**

*In both sexes*

*Plumage:* Pure white without any colour in the feathering.

*Bill:* Orange-yellow. *Legs and webs:* Orange.

**The Coloured**

Any other colour is permitted but attention should be paid to symmetry of markings.

## Weights

| | | |
|---|---|---|
| Drake | 3.2kg | (7lb) |
| Duck | 2.7kg | (6lb) |

## Scale of points

| | | |
|---|---|---|
| Carriage | 15 | |
| Head, bill and neck | 35 | [This includes 25 points for the crest] |
| Body | 15 | |
| Legs and feet | 5 | |
| Condition | 10 | |
| Colour | 10 | |
| Size | 10 | |
| | **100** | |

## Defects

Split, slipped or uneven crest. Wrong bill or leg colour in whites. Weeping eyes. Short bodies.

## Disqualifications

Any deformity, in particular twisted or kinked neck, roach back and wry tail.

# CRESTED MINIATURE

*Origin:* Britain

*Classification:* Bantam

It was created in the British Isles in the late 1980s and early 1990s. In all points it is a miniature of the large Crested.

## General characteristics: male and female

As for large Crested.

## Colour

As for large Crested.

## Weights

| | | |
|---|---|---|
| Drake | 1.1kg | ($2\frac{1}{2}$lb) |
| Duck | 0.9kg | (2lb) |

## Scale of points

| | | |
|---|---|---|
| Carriage | 15 | |
| Head, bill and neck | 30 | [This includes 25 points for the crest] |
| Body | 15 | |
| Legs and feet | 5 | |
| Condition | 10 | |
| Colour | 10 | |
| Size | 15 | |
| | **100** | |

## Defects and disqualifications

As for large Crested.

# HOOK BILL

*Origin:* Uncertain; possibly from Asia prior to being bred in large numbers at one time in Europe.

*Classification:* Light

The Hook Bill was almost certainly bred in the Netherlands in the seventeenth and eighteenth century. In old poultry books the North Holland white-breasted duck has been called the ancestor of this breed. The curved bill and white bib was deliberately bred in to assist wildfowlers in recognizing the breed while in flight. Its silhouette distinguished it from the wild mallard when the domesticated birds returned free-winged from their feeding grounds in the evening .

## General characteristics: male and female

**Carriage:** Somewhat erect.

**Head:** When viewed from the front, the skull is flat, with very little rise to the forehead. In profile, the upper neck, head and long bill are strongly curved in a semi-circle.

**Neck:** Vertical, rather long and thin.

**Body:** Medium length, fairly broad. Breast round when viewed from the front; round and full in profile, carried somewhat forward. Back long and slender; topline slightly convex. Underbody well developed, almost parallel to the back. Abdomen clear of the ground. Wings strong and carried close to the body. Tail rather broad, following the line of the back.

**Legs:** Medium length.

*Hook Bill drake and duck*

# Colour
## The White
*In both sexes*
*Plumage*: Pure white throughout.
*Bill:* White or flesh. *Legs and webs:* Bright orange.

## The Dark Mallard
*Drake*
*Head and neck:* Emerald green changing to dark green on the lower neck; this colour clear cut from the breast without a white neck ring.
*Breast:* Steel blue.
*Flanks:* Dark steel blue with dark grey stippled pencilling. Stern steel blue.
*Back:* Upper part ash colour with some green reflections. Rump green, not too shiny. Tail coverts and sex curls black with some reflections.
*Tail:* Dark grey-brown edged with light brown.
*Wings:* Primaries dark brown-grey; secondaries (speculum) dull brown with very little white bordering; tertials, coverts and scapulars dark slate blue. The scapulars are well pencilled, and tinged with brown.

*Duck*
The duck has no eye stripes. The secondaries are dull brown with very little white edging. Except for these features, the markings are the same as the mallard-coloured duck. The brown of the mallard is replaced by dark brown.

## White Bibbed Dark Mallard
The same colour as the dark mallard except for a white, heart shaped bib on the lower neck and breast The outer primaries have three to six white feathers.

*In both colours*
*Bill:* Colour in the drake slate grey with greenish tinge. In the duck, slate grey.
*Legs:* Dark orange. *Eyes:* Brown.

# Weights
| | | |
|---|---|---|
| Drake | 2.3-2.5kg | ( 5-5$\frac{1}{2}$lb) |
| Duck | 1.8-2.3kg | (3$\frac{3}{4}$-5lb) |

# Scale of points
| | |
|---|---|
| Carriage | 15 |
| Head, bill and neck | 25 |
| Body | 15 |
| Legs and feet | 5 |
| Condition | 10 |
| Colour | 20 |
| Size | 10 |
| | **100** |

# Defects
Short or straight bill. Any sign of a keel. Oversize.

# INDIAN RUNNER

*Origin:* Asia

*Classification:* Indian Runner

The era of the high egg-laying breeds of ducks started with the introduction of the Indian Runner into this country from Malaya. A ship's captain brought home fawns, fawn-and-whites and whites, distributing them among his friends in Dumfriesshire and Cumberland. They proved prolific layers, and there was a class of fawn Runners at the Dumfries show in 1876 but the fawn-and-whites were not exhibited until 1896. The Indian Runner Duck Club's Standard of 1907 described only the fawn-and-white; that of 1913 recognized also the fawn; whilst the 1930 Poultry Club Standard described the black and the chocolate varieties.

## General characteristics: male and female

**Carriage:** Upright, active, nearly perpendicular when at attention, excited or trained for the show pen. When not alarmed, or when on the move, the body may be inclined between 50-80 degrees above the horizontal. The proper carriage creates a straight line from the back of the head to the tip of the tail. Total length (fully extended in a straight line, measured from bill tip to middle toe tips): drake 65-80 cm and duck 60-70 cm.

*Note: When standing in a show pen the maximum height is closer to an extended measure from crown (above the eye) to tail tip. The following is a rough guide.*

| Bean to Toe cm (in) | Crown to Tail cm (in) |
|---|---|
| 60 (24) | 50 (20) |
| 65 (26) | 54 (21) |
| 70 (28) | 58 (23) |
| 75 (30) | 62 (24) |
| 80 (32) | 66 (26) |
| 85 (34) | 70 (28) |

**Head:** Lean and racy looking with a bill definitely wedge-shaped fitting into a skull flat on top, making a clean sweep from the top of the bill to the back of the skull. The culmen of the bill should be perfectly straight. The eye should be full, alert, bright and so high in the head that the upper part appears almost to project above the line of the skull.

**Neck:** Long, slender, in line with the body. The muscular part should be well marked, rounded and stand out from the windpipe, the extreme hardness of the feather helping to accentuate this. The neck should be neatly fitted to the head. The proportion of neck to body should be 1:2.

**Body:** Long, narrow and cylindrical along its entire length, although slightly flattened at the shoulders, funnelling gradually from body to neck. When the bird is alert the tail should extend towards the ground in a straight line from the back.

*Indian Runners - Blue, Black and White*

**Wings:** Small in relation to the size of the bird; tightly packed to the body and just crossing at the rump.

**Legs and webs:** Legs set far back to allow upright carriage. Thighs and shanks medium in length.

**Plumage:** Tight, smooth and hard.

## Colour

### The Black

*In both sexes*

*Plumage:* Black with a beetle green sheen.

*Bill:* Black. *Eyes:* Dark brown. *Legs and webs:* As black as possible.

*Colour defects*

Conspicuous white in outer plumage. Grey under chin and wings or on the secondaries and coverts. Lacing on the breast.

### The Chocolate

*In both sexes*

*Plumage:* A rich, solid chocolate throughout, darker in the drake.

*Bill:* Black. *Eyes:* Dark brown. *Legs and webs:* As black as possible.

*Colour defects*

Conspicuous white in outer plumage. Lacing.

### The Cumberland Blue

*In both sexes*

*Plumage:* Rich blue with dark shading, richest on the back. Head and upper tail cushion of the drake is a darker shade of blue.

*Bill:* Bluish green in the drake; bluish grey in the duck. *Eyes:* Dark brown.

*Legs and webs:* Smoky orange to grey.

*Colour defects*

Yellow bill. Feathers of any colour other than blue.

### The Fawn

*Drake*

*Head and neck:* Dark bronze with metallic sheen changing to rich brown-red of the lower neck and upper breast.

*Lower chest, flanks and abdomen:* French grey produced by fine stippling of sepia on a lighter ground, extending to the almost black tail under-cushion.

*Back, rump and tail:* Deep brown, almost black.

*Wings:* Primaries dark brown. Secondaries sepia with slight metallic lustre. Coverts fawn, not pencilled or laced. Scapulars red-brown, peppered.

*Bill:* Pure black to olive green mottled with black.

*Legs and webs:* Black or dark tan mottled with black.

*Duck*
The overall impression is of a uniform, warm ginger-fawn with no marked variation of shade but slightly mottled or speckled in appearance.
*Head and neck:* A shade lighter than the rest of the body; each feather has a fine line of dark red-brown, giving a ticked appearance. Lower part of the neck and the neck expansion is a shade warmer, each feather pencilled with warm red-brown.
*Lower chest and abdomen:* Same shade as head and neck; darker at the under-cushion; pencilled.
*Back, rump and tail:* Rich and well-marked pencilling, the ground colour becoming lighter and warmer towards the tail. Tail feathers light fawn, pencilled.
*Wings:* Smaller coverts lighter than the scapulars but darkening towards the greater coverts, pencilled. Secondaries warm red-brown. Primaries a shade lighter. Scapulars rich ginger-fawn, a shade darker than the shoulders and back, with well-marked red-brown pencilling.
*Bill:* Black.
*Eyes:* Golden-brown.
*Legs and webs:* Black or dark tan.

## Colour defects
White feathers. Eyebrows or eye stripes. Light or cream wing-coverts or flights. Blue or green wing bars. Orange or yellow bill, feet or legs.

## The Fawn-and-white
*In both sexes*
*Head and neck:* The cap and cheek markings in the duck are nearly the same shade of fawn as the body colour, but dull bronze-green in the drake. The cap is separated from the cheek markings by a projection from the white of the neck extending up to, and in most cases terminating in, a narrow line more or less encircling the eye. The cap should cleanly and smoothly encircle the head. The cheek markings should not extend on to the neck. The bill is divided from the head markings by a narrow prolongation of the neck-white (3-6mm wide) extending from the white underneath the chin. The neck is pure white to where the neck expansion begins, where the meeting is clean cut.
*Lower neck and body:* Uniform soft warm or ginger-fawn, produced in the male by a fine stippling of brown on the cream ground of the individual feathers. In the female the colour is the same shade as the fawn Runner duck; the feathers are pencilled, medium brown on fawn. The fawn of the thorax should meet the white of the abdomen in a clean line (near the bottom of the breast bone and the top of the thighs). The white extends between the legs to beyond the vent, and also includes the thigh coverts.
*Back, rump and tail:* The base of the neck, scapular feathers, back and rump are similar to the breast colours, although in the case of the male darkening to bronze on the rump. Tail feathers cream to medium brown in the central area. Under-cushion brown, bronze in the male.
*Thighs:* Upper thigh coverts white, tending to obscure the grey-fawn of the thighs themselves.
*Wings:* Primaries, secondaries and tertials white; smaller coverts fawn giving a rough heart shape.

*Bill:* Light orange-yellow in young birds; green-yellow in adult drakes; spotted green to almost entirely dull cucumber in adult females. Black bean.
*Eyes:* Dark brown.
*Legs and webs:* Orange-red.

### Colour defects
'Dribbles' of cap colour on to the white neck. Cheek markings extending on to the neck. Any irregular, blotchy or unclear markings that detract from the symmetry and general cleanness of the colour boundaries. Fawn extending from the back on to the abdomen and thigh coverts ('foul flanked').

## American Fawn-and-white
### In both sexes
Fawn-and-white markings distributed as in the pencilled fawn-and-white (above). Coloured feathers even fawn, including the drake's cap. Not pencilled.
*Bill, legs and webs:* As pencilled fawn-and-white Indian Runner.

## The Mallard
### Drake
*Head and neck:* Iridescent green with distinct white collar almost encircling the neck.
*Breast:* Rich claret with no white lacing.
*Flanks and abdomen:* Light grey with dark grey stippled pencilling.
*Back:* Dark grey-brown shading to greenish black over the rump and undertail.
*Tail:* Medium dull brown, paler outer feathers; coverts black.
*Wings:* Primaries and tertials grey; speculum blue bordered by black then white. Coverts brownish grey except for greater coverts which are tipped with white then black. Main scapulars clear steel grey, outer edge bronze tinge.
*Bill:* Green, dark bean.
*Eyes:* Dark brown.
*Legs and webs:* Orange-yellow.

### Duck
*Head and neck:* Golden brown, each feather with darker brown graining. This graining forms a darker band from the crown down the back of the neck. Eye stripes as in the wild mallard. Plain brown throat.
*Breast, flanks and back feathers:* brown or chestnut with dark brown pencilling on each feather. Abdomen similarly coloured.
*Tail:* Dull dark buff, irregularly marked with brown; darker tail feathers in the centre than the outer edges.
*Wings:* Primaries brownish slate, speculum and its borders as drake. Tertials browner than primaries on exposed half. Coverts same colour as back.
*Bill:* Dark orange with brown saddle.
*Eyes:* Brown.
*Legs and webs:* Somewhat darker than the drake.

Clear yellow, blue or lead-coloured bill. Any indication of a white ring in the female. White in the primaries.

## The Trout
*Drake*
*Head and neck:* Iridescent green with distinct white collar almost encircling the neck.
*Breast:* Rusty claret.
*Flanks and abdomen:* Light grey with mid grey stippled pencilling.
*Back:* Silver-grey shading to black over the rump and undertail.
*Tail:* Light on outer part, darker grey-brown on inner part.
*Wings:* Primaries and tertials grey-brown. Speculum iridescent blue bordered with black then white. Coverts silver-grey except for greater coverts which are tipped with white then black. Main scapulars silver-grey, outer edge faint bronze tinge.
*Bill:* Golden olive; dark bean.
*Eyes:* Dark brown.
*Legs and webs:* Orange-yellow.

*Duck*
*Head and neck:* Light brown, each feather with darker brown graining. This graining forms a darker band from the crown down the back of the neck. Eye stripes as in the wild mallard. Cream-fawn throat.
*Breast, flanks and back feathers:* Light fawn with dark brown, blotchy pencilling on each feather giving the impression of a central fleck. Abdomen similarly coloured.
*Tail:* Buff, irregularly marked with brown; darker tail feathers in the centre than the outer edges.
*Wings:* Primaries greyish buff. Speculum and its borders as drake. Tertials showing indications of pencilling. Coverts similar colour to back. Scapulars clearly pencilled brown on light fawn.
*Bill:* Pinkish orange-brown with spots.
*Eyes:* Brown.
*Legs and webs:* Somewhat duller than the drake.

### Colour defects
Bill dark or blue-green in the male or lead-coloured in the female. 'Mossy' or indistinct feather markings on the back of the duck's body. Dark bronze dominating scapulars of the drake.

## The White
*In both sexes*
*Plumage:* Pure white throughout
*Bill, legs and webs:* Orange-yellow. *Eyes:* blue.

### Colour defects
Any black in the drake's bill is a disqualification.
Black specks on the duck's bill are a common minor fault with age.

## Weights

| | | |
|---|---|---|
| Drake | 1.6-2.3kg | $(3\frac{1}{2}$-5lb) |
| Duck | 1.4-2.0kg | $(3$-$4\frac{1}{2}$lb) |

## Scale of points

| | |
|---|---|
| Carriage | 20 |
| Head, bill and neck | 20 |
| Body | 20 |
| Legs and feet | 5 |
| Condition | 10 |
| Colour | 15 |
| Size | 10 |
| | **100** |

## Defects

'. . . a duck which cannot maintain a natural carriage of at least 40° to the horizontal will not be considered a pure Runner, however good its other points may be . . . .'
[Indian Runner Duck Club of Great Britain]

Domed skull with central position of the eyes. Dished or Roman bill. Twisted or deformed mandibles. Thick, short or curved neck. Neck expansion that distorts the symmetry of the 'hock bottle' shape. Body squat and short, bulky, oval or flattened. Prominent shoulders. Hollow back. Legs set too far forward. Prominent thighs. Long stern. Tail turned up or inwards between the legs.

# MAGPIE

*Origin:* Wales
*Classification:* Light

The Magpie is a very striking duck with its boldly coloured and white plumage. It is a medium-sized breed which yields both meat and eggs and is a challenging bird for the shows.

## General characteristics: male and female

**Carriage:** Approximately 35 degrees when active. Good length of body, giving a somewhat racy appearance, indicative of strength combined with great activity.
**Head:** Long and straight. Eyes large and prominent, giving keen and alert appearance. Bill long and broad.
**Neck:** Long, strong and slightly curved.
**Body:** Back level and fairly broad across. Breast full and nicely rounded. Wings powerful and carried close to the body. Tail medium length, gently rising from back, and increasing apparent length of the bird.
**Legs and feet:** Medium length.
**Plumage:** Close and smooth.

*Magpie drake*

## Colour
### The Black and White
*In both sexes*
Head and neck white surmounted by a black cap covering the whole of the crown to the top of the eyes. Breast and underbody white. Back of body solid black from shoulders to the tip of the tail. White primary and secondary feathers. When the wings are closed there is a heart-shaped mantle of black feathers formed over the back. The outline of the coloured feathers should be sharp, clearly defined and symmetrical. Thighs and stern white.

### The Blue and White
As above, the blue replacing black

### The Dun and White
As above, the dun replacing black

*In both sexes and all colours*
*Bill:* Preferably yellow. In older birds: drake yellow, spotted with green and the duck grey-green.
*Eyes:* Dark grey or dark brown. *Legs and webs:* Orange.

## Weights
| | | |
|---|---|---|
| Drake | 2.5-3.2kg | $(5\frac{1}{2}-7\text{lb})$ |
| Duck | 2.0-2.7kg | $(4\frac{1}{2}-6\text{lb})$ |

## Scale of points
| | |
|---|---|
| Carriage | 10 |
| Head, bill and neck | 15 |
| Body | 15 |
| Legs and feet | 5 |
| Condition | 10 |
| Colour | 35 |
| Size | 10 |
| | **100** |

## Defects
Absence of cap; any other incorrect markings e.g. any white feathers in the tail. Cream bill. Black on legs and webs. Excessive weight or coarseness.

# MUSCOVY

*Origin:* America
*Classification:* Heavy

The Muscovy *(Cairina moschata)* has also been known as the Musk Duck and the Brazilian. It is a distinct species, unrelated to the mallard. Its wild ancestors were found in South America which must have credit for the original source. Under domestication, breeders have increased the size of the birds and also developed their colours and markings.

## General characteristics: male and female

**Carriage:** Almost horizontal, low but jaunty.
**Head:** Large, particularly in the drake. Crowned with a small crest of feathers which are raised in excitement or alarm. Caruncles on the face and over the base of the bill (both crest and caruncles more pronounced in the drake than the duck). Bill wide, strong, of medium length and slightly curved. Eyes large and bold.
**Neck:** Medium length, strong and almost erect.
**Body:** Broad, deep, very long and powerful. Breast broad, full, well rounded and carried low. Underbody long and well fleshed, clear of ground, slightly rounded. Tail long and carried low giving the body a longer appearance and a slightly curved outline to the top of the body. Wings very strong, long, and carried high. Capable of flight.
**Legs and feet:** Legs strong, wide apart and fairly short. Thighs short, strong and muscular. Feet straight, webbed, with pronounced toe nails.
**Plumage:** Close.

## Colour

Colour points to be allocated for *clarity* of the colour and the *symmetry* of the markings.

| *Both Sexes* | *Plumage* |
|---|---|
| **White-winged Black** | Dense black throughout sometimes with metallic green lustre, except for patch of white on the wing coverts. |
| **White-winged Blue** | Blue, except for patch of white on the wing coverts. |
| **White-winged Chocolate** | An even chocolate, except for patch of white on the wing coverts. |
| **Black** | Dense black throughout sometimes with metallic green lustre. |
| **White** | Pure white throughout. |
| **Blue** | Lavender or darker shade of blue throughout. |
| **Chocolate** | Even chocolate throughout. |
| **Black-and-white** | Black-and-white, with defined regularity of markings. |
| **Blue-and-white** | Lavender or darker shade of blue-and-white with defined regularity of markings. |
| **Chocolate-and-white** | Chocolate-and-white, with defined regularity of markings. |

*Muscovy drake*

*In both sexes and all colours*
*Bill:* Colour variable. Pinkish flesh or horn, sometimes with darker shading; red, yellow or black. Usually a lighter shade at the point.
*Face and caruncles:* Red sometimes with black
*Eyes:* From yellow and brown to blue.
*Legs & webs:* Variable, from yellow to black.

## Weights
Drake       4.5-6.3kg    (10-14lb)
Duck        2.3-3.2kg    (5-7lb)
It is characteristic of the breed for the drake to be about twice the size of the duck.

## Scale of points
| | | |
|---|---|---|
| Carriage | 10 | |
| Head, bill and neck | 20 | [including crest and caruncles] |
| Body | 15 | |
| Legs and feet | 5 | |
| Condition | 10 | |
| Colour | 20 | |
| Size | 20 | |
| | **100** | |

## Defects
Undersize. Uneven markings in pied birds.

# ORPINGTON

*Origin:* Great Britain
*Classification:* Light

It was from the blending of the Indian Runner, Rouen and Aylesbury that Mr. W. Cook in Kent made the buff Orpington, intending it to be a dual-purpose breed. Its introduction followed that of the khaki Campbell, and it has been said that the originator was trying to make a strain of khaki duck. At one time it was very popular for its high laying qualities combined with table qualities and also its beauty of plumage and colouring. The blue variety was also included in the 1926 Standard.

## General characteristics: male and female
**Carriage:** Slightly elevated at the shoulders, but avoiding any tendency to the upright carriage of the Pekin or Indian Runner
**Head:** Fine and oval in shape. Bill of moderate length. Eyes large and bold.
**Neck:** Moderate length, upright.
**Body:** Long and broad, deep, without any sign of a keel. Back perfectly straight. Breast full and round. Wings strong and carried closely to the sides. Tail small, compact and rising slightly from the line of the back.
**Legs and feet:** Legs of moderate length; strong.
**Plumage:** Tight and glossy.

## Colour
### *Drake*
*Plumage:* Body a rich, even shade of deep buff throughout, free from lacing, barring and pencilling. The head and neck are seal brown (two or three shades darker than the body) with a bright gloss, but complete absence of beetle green. The seal brown terminates in a sharply defined line all the way round the neck. Rump brown, as free as possible from 'blue'.
*Bill:* Yellow ochre with dark bean.

### *Duck*
*Plumage:* Body a rich even shade of buff throughout, free from blue, brown or white feathers, and any lacing.
*Bill:* Orange-brown with dark bean.

### *In both sexes*
*Eyes:* Brown. *Legs and webs:* Orange-red.

## Weights
| | | |
|---|---|---|
| Drake | 2.2-3.4kg | (5-7$\frac{1}{2}$lb) min. and max. |
| Duck | 2.2-3.2kg | (5-7lb) min. and max. |

## Scale of points
| | |
|---|---|
| Carriage | 10 |
| Head, bill and neck | 20 |
| Body | 15 |
| Legs and feet | 5 |
| Condition | 10 |
| Colour | 30 |
| Size | 10 |
| | **100** |

## Defects
*In both sexes:* Colour other than stated.
*In the drake:* Grey, silver or blue head. White feathers in the neck. Brown secondaries. Beetle green on any part. Blue rump. Very green bill.
*In the duck:* Lacing. Line over the eyes. White feathers on the neck or breast. Brown or blue feathers. Green bill.

*Buff Orpington duck and drake*

# PEKIN

*Origin:* Asia

*Classification:* Heavy

Bred in China, the Pekin reached this country around 1874 and about the same time stock also went to America where it became the producer of high-class table ducklings.

## General Characteristics: male and female

**Carriage:** Almost upright.

**Head:** Large, broad and round, with high skull, rising rather abruptly from the base of the bill. Erect nape feathers, especially on the drake, can give the impression of a mane. Bill short, broad and thick, slightly convex or straight. Eyes bold, partly shaded by heavy brows and bulky cheeks.

**Neck:** Appears short and thick; with slightly gulleted throat.

**Body:** Broad and of medium length. Breast broad, smooth and full, followed in underline by the keel which shows very slightly between the legs. Broad deep paunch and stern carried just clear of the ground. Wings short, carried closely to the sides. Tail well spread and carried high. A good description of the general shape of the Pekin is that it resembles a small, wide boat, standing almost on its stern, and the bow leaning slightly forward.

**Legs and feet:** Legs strong and stout, set well back and causing erect carriage.

**Plumage:** Very abundant.

## Colour

***In both sexes***

*Plumage:* Deep cream or cream.

*Bill:* Bright orange. *Eyes:* Dark lead blue. *Legs and webs:* Bright orange.

## Weights

| | | |
|---|---|---|
| Drake | 4.1kg | (9lb) |
| Duck | 3.6kg | (8lb) |

## Scale of points

| | |
|---|---|
| Carriage | 20 |
| Head, bill and neck | 20 |
| Body | 15 |
| Legs and feet | 5 |
| Condition | 10 |
| Colour | 10 |
| Size | 20 |
| | **100** |

## Defects

Black marks or spots on bill. Long or dished bill.

*Pekin drake*

# ROUEN

*Origin:* France
*Classification:* Heavy

The Rouen was developed from the wild mallard which it closely resembles in plumage markings. The breed undoubtedly comes from Rouen in France, and was known also as the Rhone duck. When first brought to England from France the breed was developed for table properties and was used in table crossings. Later it was bred, as today, for beauty of plumage and of markings.

## General characteristics: male and female
**Carriage:** Horizontal, the keel parallel to and touching the ground.
**Head:** Massive. Bill long, wide and flat. Eyes bold.
**Neck:** Medium length, strong, slightly curved but not arched.
**Body:** Long and broad. Keel deep. Breast broad and deep. Wings large and well tucked to the sides. Tail very slightly elevated.
**Legs and feet:** Legs of medium length. Shanks stout and well set to balance the body in a straight line.
**Plumage:** Tight and glossy.

## Colour
*Drake*
*Head and neck:* Rich iridescent green to within about 2.5cm (1in) of the shoulders where the ring appears.
*Ring:* Perfectly white and cleanly cut, dividing the neck and breast colours, but not quite encircling the neck.
*Breast:* Rich claret, in the form of a deep, cleanly cut bib.
*Flanks and stern:* Grey charcoal stippled pencilling on lighter ground.
*Back and rump:* Rich green-black. Rump under-cushion black, separated by indistinct, curved line.
*Tail:* Dark slate brown. Tail coverts: black or dark slate tinged with brown; two or three green-black curled feathers in the centre.
*Wings:*
Primaries and primary coverts dark brown slate.
Secondaries (speculum) iridescent blue tipped with distinct black then white bars.
Greater coverts brown slate tipped with distinct white then black bars.
Smaller coverts grey.
Scapular feathers similar to, but more brown than, the flank feathers. At the centre of the back and on the edges above the wings, these are rich, dark bronze.

Markings throughout the whole plumage should be cleanly cut and well defined in every detail, the colours distinct and not shading into each other.

*Bill:* Bright green-yellow, with black bean at the tip. *Eyes:* Dark hazel.
*Legs and webs:* Orange-red.

*Rouen drake*

*Rouen duck*

*Duck*
*Head and neck:* Rich golden or chestnut brown, each feather with darker brown graining. This graining forms a darker band from the bill over the crown, the band becoming less distinct down the back of the neck. Faint eye stripes i.e. a paler line above the eye, a dark line through the eye and a pale line in front of the eye. Plain, lighter throat.
*Wings:*
Primaries and primary coverts dark brown slate.
Secondaries (speculum) iridescent blue tipped with distinct black then white bars.
Greater coverts brown slate tipped with distinct white then black bars.
Smaller coverts laced with a lighter colour.
*Remainder of plumage:* Rich golden or chestnut brown, every feather distinctly pencilled from breast to flank and stern, the markings to be very dark brown to black, the black pencilling on the rump having a green lustre. Large feathers ideally show double or triple pencilling (chevrons).
*Bill:* Orange, with black bean at tip, and black saddle extending almost to each side and about two thirds down towards the tip.
*Eyes:* Dark hazel. *Legs and webs:* Dull orange-brown.

## Weights
| | | |
|---|---|---|
| Drake | 4.5-5.4kg | (10-12lb) |
| Duck | 4.1-5kg | (9-11lb) |

## Scale of points
| | |
|---|---|
| Carriage | 10 |
| Head, bill and neck | 15 |
| Body | 10 |
| Legs and feet | 5 |
| Condition | 10 |
| Colour | 35 |
| Size | 15 |
| | **100** |

## Defects
*In both sexes:* White on primaries. Indistinct secondary or greater covert bars.
*In the drake:* White fringing on claret breast feathers. Claret colour running into the body colour. Flank feathers with white or rust. Lack of neck ring. Blue-green in the colour of the bill.
*In the duck:* White or approaching white ring on neck. Indistinct or insufficient pencilling. Leaden bill.

# ROUEN CLAIR

*Origin:* France
*Classification:* Heavy

It must remind one of a light-coloured common mallard—a body long and developed, the width corresponding with the length.

## General characteristics: male and female

**Carriage:** Rather more upright than the Rouen, ten to twenty degrees above the horizontal.
**Body:** Very long, graceful with good width, yet more smooth breasted than the Rouen. The important feature of the Rouen Clair is its length (ideally 90 cm [35 inches] from the point of beak to the end of tail with neck extended) which gives it elegance in spite of its heavy body. Wings neatly folded; long in proportion to the body. Tail moderately spread when bird is relaxed.
**Head:** Bold, eyes alert; bill medium length, broad.
**Neck:** Upright and of medium length; not thin.
**Legs and feet:** Legs average length, set slightly back.
**Plumage:** Fairly tight.

## Colour

### Drake

*Head and neck:* Green with clear white collar covering about four-fifths of the neck - no grey in the green
*Breast:* Red chestnut, with light white border at the end of each feather.
*Flanks:* Pearly grey (grey stippled pencilling on lighter ground). No mixture of chestnut feathers. Stern white.
*Underbody:* Light grey changing to white.
*Back:* Pearly grey, darker than the flanks. Rump brilliant greenish black. Undertail black.
*Tail:* Whitish grey.
*Wings:*
Primaries greyish brown with light edge.
Secondaries (speculum) violet blue (indigo) with brilliant reflecting powers; tipped with black then white bars. Greater coverts form black and white upper bar. Tertials grey.
Smaller coverts greyish brown.
Scapulars grey with bronze edge.
*Bill:* Yellow with greenish tint and no black lines along its centre; black bean.
*Eyes:* Yellow-brown. *Legs and webs:* Orange-yellow.

### Duck

*Head and neck:* Dark fawn with dark graining on the crown. Eye brow of creamy white; pale line in front of the eye to the bill; dark line through the eye. Top of the bill and front of neck creamy fawn (this colour not extending too low on the breast).
*Body:* Fawn ground, delicately streaked or pencilled with dark brown. Pencilling best developed on the larger feathers.
*Tail:* Colour as body.

*Rouen Clair duck and drake*

*Wings:*
Primaries greyish brown with light edges.
Speculum as drake. Coverts brown edged with cream.
Scapulars ideally pencilled with a single V in brown.
*Bill*: Orange ochre with brown saddle; black bean. *Eyes:* Dark brown.
*Legs and webs:* Dull yellow-orange.

## Weights

| | | |
|---|---|---|
| Drake | 3.4-4.1kg | $(7\frac{1}{2}-9lb)$ |
| Duck | 2.9-3.4kg | $(6\frac{1}{2}-7\frac{1}{2}lb)$ |

## Scale of points

| | |
|---|---|
| Carriage | 10 |
| Head, bill and neck | 15 |
| Body | 15 |
| Legs and feet | 5 |
| Condition | 10 |
| Colour | 30 |
| Size | 15 |
| | **100** |

## Defects

*In both sexes:* White flights. Lack of size. Presence of keel.
*In the drake:* Lack of white stern.
*In the duck:* Lack of eye stripes.

# SAXONY

*Origin:* Germany
*Classification:* Heavy

As the name suggests the Saxony was developed in this region of Germany in the early 1930s. It is therefore a relatively new breed and made its first public appearance at the Saxony County Show in 1934. It is a dual purpose domestic duck, attractive in appearance, producing full-breasted, meaty birds and not less than 150 eggs per year.

## General characteristics: male and female

**Carriage:** Almost horizontal when at rest; elevated to approximately 30 degrees when active and alert.
**Head:** Long, flat and bold. Bill average length and broad. Eyes bright.
**Neck:** Average length, same width from head to breast, not thin.
**Body:** Large, broad and deep without any suggestion of a keel. Breast full and round. The wings strong, compact and carried close to the body. Tail long and closed.
**Legs and feet:** Medium length. Legs set a little back from centre.
**Plumage:** Close and smooth.

*Saxony duck*

*Saxony drake*

## Colour

*Drake*

Head and neck blue-grey down to neck ring which is white and about 5mm ($\frac{1}{4}$ inch) wide. This ring should encircle the whole of the neck. The lower neck (below ring), breast and shoulders are rusty red with slight silver lacing on the shoulders and breast. Lower body oatmeal. Back, rump and undercushion blue-grey. Stern white. Flights grey with darker speculum. Tail light grey.

*Duck*

Head, neck and breast deep apricot buff with a white eye line above the eye and also a lower one in front of the eye. Throat cream. Back and rump paler buff. Secondaries pale grey, flights oatmeal. Tail buff.

*In both sexes*

*Bill:* Yellow. *Eyes:* Dark brown. *Legs and webs:* Orange.

## Weights

| | | |
|---|---|---|
| Drake | 3.6kg | (8lb) |
| Duck | 3.2kg | (7lb) |

## Scale of points

| | |
|---|---|
| Carriage | 10 |
| Head, bill and neck | 15 |
| Body | 15 |
| Legs and feet | 5 |
| Condition | 10 |
| Colour | 30 |
| Size | 15 |
| | **100** |

## Defects

*In both sexes:* Keel. Black bean on bill. Coloured nostrils. Pale eyes. Upright carriage.
*In the drake:* Broken neck ring. Brown in head. Breast colour running onto the flanks and solid breast colour.
*In the duck:* Excessive white on breast. Absence of eye stripes.

## Disqualifications

*In the drake:* Absence of neck ring.
*In the duck:* Presence of neck ring.

# SILVER APPLEYARD

*Origin:* Great Britain
*Classification:* Heavy

The Silver Appleyard is a good all-round utility duck originally produced by Reginald Appleyard from selective cross breeding. It is a good layer, an excellent table bird and very ornamental.

## General characteristics: male and female
**Carriage:** Lively, slightly erect, the back sloping gently from shoulder to tail.
**Body:** Compact, broad and well rounded. Moderate length. Tail broad, slightly elevated.
**Head:** Bold, eyes alert. Bill medium length, broad.
**Neck:** Upright and of medium length, not thin.
**Legs and feet:** Legs average length, set slightly back.
**Plumage:** Tight.

## Colour
*Drake*

*Head and neck:* Black-green with a silver-white flecked throat. Faint eye brow and cheek markings in silver. A silver-white ring completely encircles the neck. Base of neck and shoulders below the ring claret.
*Breast:* The claret colour of the shoulders tips the feathers of the breast which have a white under-colour. Each feather has a very fine white fringe. Broken claret bib fades to silver under the body.
*Flanks:* Grey stippled pencilling on white ground. Claret of breast extends along the upper flank above the thigh coverts which are pale grey.
*Back:* Laced claret replaced by dark grey mottled back feathers. Rump solid black-green. Undertail black-green.
*Tail:* Grey with broad white edging.
*Wings:*
Primaries grey and white, with white edging.
Secondaries (speculum) iridescent blue tipped with black then white.
Tertials grey.
Silver light wing coverts match the breast and underbody.
Scapulars grey stipple; outer edge chestnut.
*Bill:* Yellow-green.

*Duck*

*Head and neck:* Silver-white with crown and back of neck fawn flecked with brown-grey. This fawn on the neck to join the shoulder without a noticeable break. Fawn line through the eye.
*Breast and underbody:* Creamy white
*Flanks:* Creamy white or fawn, flecked with brown-grey.
*Back and rump:* Fawn flecked with brown-grey.
*Tail:* Mottled fawn, darker centre to each feather.

*Large Silver Appleyard drake and duck*

*Wings:*
Primaries creamy white, brown towards the tip.
Secondaries (speculum) blue, tipped with black then white.
Tertials mottled fawn-brown.
Coverts white, marked with fawn and grey.
Scapulars fawn streaked with grey-brown.
*Bill:* Yellow with brown saddle.

**In both sexes**
*Eyes:* Dark hazel. *Legs:* Orange.

## Weights

| Drake | 3.6-4.1kg | (8-9lb) |
|-------|-----------|---------|
| Duck  | 3.2-3.6kg | (7-8lb) |

## Scale of points

| | |
|---|---|
| Carriage | 10 |
| Head, bill and neck | 15 |
| Body | 15 |
| Legs and feet | 5 |
| Condition | 10 |
| Colour | 30 |
| Size | 15 |
| | **100** |

## Defects

*In both sexes:* Absence of blue speculum. Presence of keel. Undersize.
*In the drake:* Lack of silver cheek and throat markings.
*In the duck:* Lack of eye stripe. Brown head and neck.

# SILVER APPLEYARD MINIATURE

*Origin:* Britain
*Classification:* Bantam

These are a miniature of the large Appleyard, with general characteristics and colour as for the large. They were developed by Tom Bartlett in the 1980s and shown at the Champion Waterfowl Exhibition in 1987.

## Weights

| Drake | 1.4kg | (3lb) |
|-------|-------|-------|
| Duck  | 1.1kg | ($2\frac{1}{2}$lb) |

*Silver Appleyard Miniature drake and duck*

## Scale of points

| | |
|---|---|
| Carriage | 10 |
| Head, bill and neck | 15 |
| Body | 15 |
| Legs and feet | 5 |
| Condition | 10 |
| Colour | 30 |
| Size | 15 |
| | **100** |

## Defects

*In both sexes:* Absence of blue speculum. Presence of broad band of white extending up the back of the neck. Over-size; similarity with the mallard—long beak and racy body.
*In the drake:* Lack of silver cheek, throat markings or eye stripe.
*In the duck:* Brown head and neck.

# SILVER BANTAM

*Origin:* Great Britain
*Classification:* Bantam

This bantam breed was formerly known as the Silver Appleyard Bantam. It was originally produced by Reginald Appleyard as a cross between a small khaki Campbell and a white Call drake in the 1940s.

## General characteristics: male and female

**Carriage:** Sprightly, slightly erect, head held high, the back sloping gently from the shoulder to the tail. Body clear of the ground for active foraging.
**Head:** Small and neat; bill medium length.
**Neck:** Medium length, almost vertical.
**Body:** Compact, but a more slender shape than the Call duck. Tail short and small.
**Legs and feet:** Legs short, set midway in the body.
**Plumage:** Tight.

## Colour

*Drake*
*Head and neck:* Dark, glossy green; terminated by a neat white collar completely encircling the neck.
*Breast and shoulders:* Broken red-brown with white lacing.
*Flanks, underbody and stern:* Silver white; some red-brown feathers interspersed with the white on the flanks.
*Back:* Grey with black stippling. Rump and undertail black.
*Tail:* Grey, edged with white.
*Wings:* Primaries white with grey stippling on outer edge. Violet-green speculum. Scapulars grey stipple; outer edge chestnut.
*Bill:* Yellow-green, black bean.

*Duck*
*Head and neck:* Fawn with dark brown or black graining
*Breast and shoulders:* Cream with brown streaks.
*Flanks, underbody and stern:* Creamy white.
*Back:* Creamy white. Rump creamy white to fawn-grey with brown flecks.
*Tail:* Mottled fawn.
*Wings:* Primaries and speculum as drake. Smaller coverts dark fawn and grey-fawn with cream lacing. Scapulars cream streaked with brown.
*Bill:* Yellow to grey-green, with black markings on the saddle.

### In both sexes
*Eyes:* Dark brown. *Legs:* Orange.

## Weights
| | | |
|---|---|---|
| Drake | 0.9kg | (2lb) |
| Duck | 0.8kg | (1¾lb) |

## Scale of points
| | |
|---|---|
| Carriage | 10 |
| Head, bill and neck | 15 |
| Body | 15 |
| Legs and feet | 5 |
| Condition | 10 |
| Colour | 30 |
| Size | 15 |
| | **100** |

## Defects
*In both sexes:* Oversize.
*In the duck:* Insufficient colour.

# WELSH HARLEQUIN

*Origin:* British
*Classification:* Light

The Welsh Harlequin was developed at the end of the Second World War by Group Captain Bonnet from 'sports' of the khaki Campbell. Almost lost in its original form, the breed was rescued by Eddie Grayson.

## General characteristics: male and female
**Carriage:** Alert and slightly upright, the head carried high with shoulders higher than the saddle, the back showing a gentle slant; the whole carriage not too erect but not so low as to cause waddling. Activity and foraging power to be retained without loss of depth and width of body generally.
**Head:** Refined in jaw and skull. Bill of medium length, depth and width: set in a straight line with the top of the skull. Eyes full, bold and bright; fairly high in skull and prominent.

**Neck:** Medium length, slender, almost erect.
**Body:** Compact, with width well maintained from shoulders to stern. Tail short and small.
**Legs and feet:** Legs medium length and set well apart; not too far back.
**Plumage:** Tight and silky, giving a sleek appearance.

## Colour
### Drake
*Head and upper neck:* Iridescent green overlaid with bronze lustre to within about 2.5 cm (1in) of the shoulders where a 0.5-1.5 cm ($\frac{1}{4}$-$\frac{1}{2}$ in) white ring (finer and more clearly defined at the front than the back) completely encircles the neck.
*Breast, neck base and shoulders:* Rich red-brown mahogany, finely laced with white. This colour washes along the upper flank, finishing at the upper thigh coverts.
*Underbody and stern:* Creamy white.
*Lower back:* Slate grey as it meets the rump, which is beetle green. 'Sex curls' same colour as the rump.
*Tail:* Dark brown bordered with white; undertail cushion beetle green.
*Wings:* Primaries off-white, overlaid with brown. Speculum bronze with green lustre, bordered by very fine line of white. Wing coverts light mahogany laced with creamy white. Scapulars and tertials as the breast colour, laced with creamy white which gives a rich tortoiseshell effect.
*Bill:* Olive green without any trace of blue; black bean at the tip.
*Eyes:* Dark brown. *Legs and webs:* Orange.

### Duck
*Head and upper neck:* Honey-fawn with brown graining on the crown.
*Main body feathers:* Fawn to cream; central shaft of feathers marked with brown. These markings less distinct on breast and underbody .
*Rump:* Mid-brown with darker brown central streak to each feather.
*Tail:* Mid-brown.
*Wings:* Primaries brown edged with white, slightly darker than the drake. Speculum bronze. Well defined lacing on the wing coverts. Scapulars a mixture of fawn, red-brown and cream producing a rich, tortoiseshell effect.
N.B. The general body colour becomes quite diluted when the female is in full egg production.
*Bill:* Gun metal / slate grey. *Eyes:* Dark brown.
*Legs and webs:* Dark brown in mature stock.

## Weights
| | | |
|---|---|---|
| Adult drake | 2.3-2.5kg | (5-5$\frac{1}{2}$lb) |
| Adult duck | 2.0-2.3kg | (4$\frac{1}{2}$-5lb) |

*Welsh Harlequin drake and duck*

## Scale of points

| | |
|---|---|
| Carriage | 10 |
| Head, bill and neck | 15 |
| Body | 15 |
| Legs and feet | 5 |
| Condition | 10 |
| Colour | 35 |
| Size | 10 |
| | **100** |

## Defects

*In both sexes:* Upright carriage. Lack of lacing on small wing coverts. Presence of blue speculum. Oversize or keel.

*In the drake:* Broken or absent neck ring. Blue bill.

*In the duck:* Lack of dark feather markings on the rump. Lack of graining on the head. Bill other than slate. Orange legs (legs are palest in younger birds; they darken with age).

# Other Breeds

The British Waterfowl Association looks after any other breeds of duck not standardized in this edition. Specimens of other breeds appear occasionally, but not so far in sufficient numbers to warrant standardizing.

### Pommern

A small Blue Swedish without white flights; Eastern European in origin.

### Shetland

A small and less well marked version of the Blue Swedish, but black where the Swedish is blue.

# Glossary

| | |
|---|---|
| **A.O.C.** | Any Other Colour |
| **A.O.V.** | Any Other Variety |
| **abdomen** | the lower body, below the thorax, from keel to vent |
| **angel wing** | see **oar wing** |
| **auto-sexing** | Sexual dichromatism in the plumage; males a different colour or pattern from the female |
| **back** | (a) the dorsal surface of the body not including the wings; <br> (b) (rarely) the wings folded above the body (e.g. Buff Back) |
| **bar** | a narrow horizontal stripe across a feather |
| **bean** | raised, hard, oval protuberance at the tip of the upper mandible of a waterfowl |
| **bill** | horny projection consisting of upper and lower mandibles forming the mouth parts of a bird |
| **breast** | the ventral area of the thorax or chest |
| **breed** | variety with genetically stable phenotype |
| **carriage** | posture; angle of the body to the horizontal. |
| **caruncles** | fleshy protuberances on the face of a Muscovy or turkey |
| **collar** | a band of colour partially or completely encircling the neck |
| **condition** | healthy appearance, particularly of the plumage |
| **coverts** | feathers which cover the wings, the upper leg, and overlap the main tail feathers. See also **wing coverts** |
| **crest** | feathers above the upper surface of the cranium; tufted outgrowth on the head |
| **culmen** | longitudinal ridge of the bill |
| **dewlap** | fold or flap of loose skin below the lower mandible |
| **dished bill** | concave culmen |
| **down** | the layer of soft plumage, without stem or stiff herl, lying below the main feathers |
| **drake** | male of the anatine species |
| **dropped tongue** | the tongue drops and is trapped in the cavity of the lower mandible. This impedes eating |
| **dual-lobed** | paunch made up of two balanced and symmetrical folds |
| **duck** | female of the anatine species |
| **eclipse** | dull summer plumage of coloured drakes |
| **flights** | primary and secondary wing feathers; <br> long, stiff feathers with little or no down; these are anchored by connective tissue to the bone; the vanes are largely of unequal width. They include the wing flights (remiges), primary, secondary and tertial feathers, as well as the tail flights (rectrices). The term is frequently used to indicate primaries only. |
| **frizzled** | curled or twisted feathers, usually caused by splitting of the stems |
| **gander** | male of anserine species |
| **goose** | female of anserine species |
| **greater coverts** | the wing coverts immediately overlapping the **secondaries**, sometimes referred to as the 'wing bar' |
| **ground colour** | base colour of the feather on to which the bars, stipples etc. are foregrounded |

| | |
|---|---|
| **gullet** | oesophagus; throat; (sometimes) dewlap |
| **hock** | ankle joint, between 'thigh' and 'shank' |
| **keel** | carina; ridge along the breast bone; (in ducks and geese) deep, pendant fold of skin and tissue suspended along the sternum |
| **knob** | globular, fleshy protuberance above the base of the upper mandible, in African and Chinese geese |
| **lacing** | a stripe along the very edge of the feather. |
| **leg** | the lower part of the hind limb, including thigh, hock, shank and foot |
| **lesser coverts** | the small covert feathers between the median and marginal coverts |
| **lobe** | round or pendulous fold, usually of the paunch |
| **lustre** | sheen |
| **mandibles** | upper and lower parts of the bill |
| **marginal coverts** | the smallest covert feathers on the leading edge of the wing |
| **median coverts** | the line of coverts immediately overlapping the greater coverts |
| **mossy** | degraded pencilling or other marking; indistinct or chaotic patterns |
| **nape** | back of the neck |
| **oar wing** | deformity of the lower joint of the wing causing the primaries to stick out like oars (often the result of high protein feeding and extremely rapid growth in young birds). See also **angel wing** and **slipped wing**. |
| **paunch** | pendulous folds below the lower abdomen |
| **pencilling** | fine stripes or bands that are either concentric, following the outline of the feather (as in the Rouen duck), or across the feather (as in the pencilled Hamburg chicken) |
| **preen gland** | gland situated at the base of a bird's tail and producing oil used in preening; uropygial gland |
| **primaries** | outer flight feathers beyond the carpal joint or 'wrist' |
| **primary coverts** | the coverts immediately overlapping the **primaries** |
| **quill** | central stem of a feather |
| **reach** | overall height |
| **roach back** | convex distortion of the spine, usually of the lumbar vertebrae |
| **rump** | lower back, immediately above the tail |
| **saddle** | a patch of colour across the lower back or across the culmen of the bill |
| **sappiness** | yellow tinge in the white plumage |
| **scapulars** | feathers in the shoulder region, usually shielding a large area of the wing when folded |
| **secondaries** | inner flight feathers attached to the radius/ulna region of the wing; the speculum |
| **self colour** | a single colour or shade covering the main plumage |
| **serrations** | saw-like grooves or notches in the mandibles |
| **sex curls** | the distinct curls above the tails of mallard drakes |
| **shaft** | central stem |
| **shank** | lower leg (tarso-metatarsus) |
| **sheen** | glistening reflections, lustre |
| **slipped wing** | 'wing in which the primary feathers hang below the secondaries when the wing is closed' (British Poultry Standards). Also, there may be a permanent tendency for the entire primary section of the wing to be held outside the secondaries (American Poultry Association). In Waterfowl, this term is sometimes used to describe **angel wing** |

| | |
|---|---|
| **smaller coverts** | secondary coverts including median and lesser coverts |
| **speculum** | iridescent secondary feathers of the mallard |
| **split crest** | crest made up of more than one central tuft |
| **stern** | area near the vent, below the tail |
| **stippled pencilling** | lines or bands of small dots (e.g. on mallard drake flanks) |
| **stippling** | small dots |
| **strain** | sub-variety or closed flock within a breed |
| **tail coverts** | feathers which immediately overlap the main tail feathers |
| **tertials** | main feathers from the innermost wing joint |
| **thigh** | section of the leg: (in birds) the area of the tibia; (in mammals) the area of the femur |
| **ticked** | having small, slightly elongated marks |
| **trio** | group of three, specifically one male and two females |
| **type** | the general shape or form; the proportion of parts to the whole; those elements of shape that *typify* the breed; the *gestalt*. |
| **undercolour** | colour of the fluff below the main herls of the feather |
| **uropygium** | rump; coccyx; tip of the caudal vertebrae |
| **web** | area of skin between the toes; (of feathers) interlocking fabric of barbs or herls |
| **wing coverts** | contour feathers covering the wing or overlapping the wing flights. |
| **wry back** | twisted or distorted spine |
| **wry tail** | tail and spine-tip out of line with the rest of the back-bone |